CHAVA'S STORY

CHAVA'S STORY

a gripping novel, portraying life in the
Soviet Union during the past century

by
Estelle Chasen

ISBN: 0 87306-826-2

Distributed by
Philip Feldheim Inc.
200 Airport Executive Park
Nanuet N.Y., 10954

Feldheim Publishers Ltd.
P.O.B. 35002 Jerusalem Israel
Printed in Israel

TABLE OF CONTENTS

FOREWORD

My first book, THE LONG ROAD HOME, was a novel about a young girl, Rivka, and her life in the Kovno Ghetto, Lithuania, during the Second World War. CHAVA'S STORY traces the life of Rivka's friend, Chava, whose family decided to run deeper into Russian territory to escape the Nazi onslaught. Although the two narratives are connected, they may easily be read as separate entities.

Doing the research for this novel was a fascinating learning experience. I made use of a number of books written over the years which painstakingly recorded the suffering of the Jewish people during the Communist regime. After Perestroika, when it became possible to speak out, a number of wonderful people such as Basya Barg, Aaron Chazan and Eliyahu Essas shared their heroic lives with us by telling their stories. All these precious documents inspired me greatly.

The amazing history of Russian Jewry during this century is only starting to be told. The fact that many of our people became lost to their faith is common knowledge. What is less well known, however, is just what a huge population of our people remained in the Soviet Union after the Holocaust. Also, we are only now becoming aware of the extent of personal suffering, heroism and sacrifice endured by many in order to uphold Yiddishkeit, maintain their identity and continue to forge the links between themselves and their homeland, Israel.

It is to all these modern day tzaddikim and heroes that I dedicate this novel.

CHAVA'S STORY

CHAPTER ONE

Chava Bernstein peered intently out of the train window, her gaze fixed on a small speck, which just a few minutes earlier had held the form of her tearful friend, Rivka.

Although her eyes were fixed on the distance, her mind focussed on a scene from the previous evening, when she had tried to comfort Rivka.

"War doesn't last forever, Rivki," she had said as Rivka helped her to pack. "A few weeks, at worst maybe a few months. I'm sure we'll see each other again when we're both fifteen," she had added optimistically.

"Still, I wish your family were coming, too. I wish you were moving deeper into the Soviet Union like us. Look at what the Germans have been doing to the Jews of Poland!" She shook her head as she folded a pretty skirt into her suitcase.

"Yes, but that kind of thing won't happen here, Chava. You can't imagine that if Hitler attacks the mighty Soviet Union, he's going to have time to bother specifically about the Jews. The Jews of Lithuania have played their part in the society here. Nothing terrible can happen. Besides, my Pappa says he doesn't know who's worse, Hitler or Stalin. Since the revolution, Jews have been forbidden to practise *mitzvos*, even the basic ones like Shabbos and Bris

Milah. Who knows if life will be better closer to the Kremlin."

"So," Chava said with a sigh. "Hitler attacks our bodies, Stalin our souls. What a choice we have!"

It was then Rivka's turn to attempt to lighten the conversation. "Miss Bernstein," she said with a smile on her face, "it occurs to me that you have not taken a dress for the Opera House in Sverdlovsk!"

"Who knows if there even is an Opera House in Sverdlovsk," Chava said wearily.

"But of course there will be an Opera House in Sverdlovsk!" said Rivka. "There's no Russian town without a Music Theatre or Opera House. The Russian people cannot live without their music and theatre!"

"All right, I'll take a smart dress, although if there's a war, there certainly won't be any music or theatre!" Chava packed her prettiest dress neatly into her small suitcase.

The train lurched and brought Chava back to the present. The speck in the distance had disappeared. The train had already reached the outskirts of Kovno.

She turned back to the noisy, cramped compartment which her family was sharing with the Feldman family, a young couple with three small children under the age of four.

Her eighteen year old brother, Maish, got up and gave her his seat next to her mother.

"How do you feel now, Mamma?" Chava asked her mother.

"Oh, not so bad, my darling," Nechama Bernstein replied. But her face was grey with pain. The whole family knew how badly she was suffering with stomach ulcers, a condition worsened by the anxiety of the previous weeks.

Chava's father, Sholem, winked at her reassuringly. Mrs. Feldman, looking rather harassed in the trying circumstances, tried to cheer Chava up. "Have some sandwiches, my dear," she kindly offered. "And here, take a cup of the warm strong coffee I prepared. That will make you feel better."

The food and warm drink did strangely comfort her. She felt the lump in her throat subside. Her butterflies disappeared. She watched quietly as the Feldman children played on the floor in the centre of the compartment. Finally she put her head on her mother's shoulder and drifted off to sleep. Half an hour later, she awoke to the sound of her parents deep in discussion with the Feldmans.

"It will be no trouble at all, I assure you," she heard Mr. Feldman say quietly. "In the same way my brother has found accommodation for us in Odessa, I'm sure he'll find accommodation for you. It's a long, long ride to Sverdlovsk and Mrs. Bernstein is just not up to it."

Chava's eyes flew open and she sat bolt upright. Were her parents now talking about going to Odessa in the Ukraine, not far from the Russian border? How could they change their plans so suddenly and radically? Then she looked at her mother's ashen face and understood. There was no alternative. It would have to be Odessa.

All the way to Minsk, Chava watched her father. His eyes were pensive and worried. And the crowded train lurched on with its load of soldiers and refugees.

At Minsk, the two families with their copious baggage changed trains and headed for Odessa. This time there was standing room only, except for the sick and the elderly, so Nechama sat, while the rest of them held on to the nearest support, trying to keep their balance. Chava's offer to hold baby Basha for

Mrs. Feldman was gratefully accepted. The two parents had their hands full watching over their two energetic little boys.

"Just don't forget she's still a tiny baby and her neck is not yet strong. Support the back of her head," Mrs. Feldman said.

Chava held Basha in the crook of her left arm. Her right hand clasped the back of a seat for anchorage and balance. She crooned softly to Basha until she thought the little one had fallen asleep. Then she turned slightly and listened to the conversation her father was having with her brother Maish.

"No, Maish," Sholem was saying. "I thought about this change in our plans all the way to Minsk, and things aren't as bad as they could be. It's true I felt more certain of our future in Sverdlovsk because I'd arranged accommodation for the family, and organized work for myself at a dental clinic. But quite honestly, I don't know now whether we would have managed to find places on a train to Sverdlovsk. The trains are so crowded, we might have had to wait for days in Minsk to find transport. We'll manage in Odessa. Some kind people will assist us, even if the Feldmans can't. Don't we always help each other?

"On the way to Minsk, I tried to remember everything I'd ever heard about Odessa. Listen to this!" he said to Maish and Chava. "Before the revolution, do you know what they used to say about a man whose taste for the good life was matched by his good fortune? They'd say '*Er lebt vi G-t in Odess*'. He lives like G-d in Odessa. As though even G-d himself was happiest there.

"Until the revolution, the Jewish community of Odessa was the second largest in the whole of Russia. Hundreds of thousands of Jews lived there - Orthodox and freethinkers, Chassidim and Misnagdim, Litvaks, Polish Jews and Galicians. It's a cosmopolitan harbour city, where at one stage everybody belonged to one ethnic minority group or another, so Odessa Jews have always felt very much at home. They didn't have to be apologetic or defensive."

He became quite excited now. "Yes," he continued, "spiritual freedom and broadmindedness in the city did give rise to a lot of assimilation on the one hand, but on the other hand it created an atmosphere for inspiring great innovations. It was in Odessa that the first Hebrew newspaper appeared. And it was Odessa that was home to Hebrew poets like Bialik, thinkers and writers like Achad Ha'am and Sholem Aleichem, and famous Zionists like Pinsker and Jabotinsky!"

At this almost lyrical outburst of enthusiasm, Maish and Chava both raised their eyebrows and began to roll their eyes sceptically.

Sholem laughed. "All right," he said, "there's also the saying that a man could have the soles of his shoes cut off while walking the streets of Odessa. It's true that Odessa used to have an efficient underworld of thieves, crooks and cheaters, but the Communists have probably put a stop to all that."

"But what about pogroms, Pappa?" Maish asked quietly.

"Aha!" Sholem retorted, triumphantly. "After the revolution, a Jewish self-defence unit was formed. So, while thousands upon thousands of Jews died in antisemitic outbursts in the Ukraine during the terrible Civil War, there were no pogroms in Odessa!"

Her father's apparent confidence cheered Chava up. Still, she felt tired and the arm that held Basha was beginning to ache. She repositioned her feet in order to gain better balance.

"How long will it be till we reach Odessa, Pappa?" she asked.

"Only another hour, Chavale. Not long at all now."

Chava was immensely relieved. When the train stopped briefly at a siding to pick up soldiers, she changed Basha to her other arm, and waited hopefully for the journey to end.

As the train lurched forward again, she whispered more to herself than to the baby. "It's going to be all right in Odessa, Bashi. You'll see. It's going to be all right."

CHAPTER TWO

Lying on her mattress that night, Chava waited for sleep to come, but it eluded her. The traumatic events of the day kept going through her mind - the train journeys, their arrival in Odessa, the ride in the trolley car all the way to the Moldavanka section of the city where they had alighted at Sholom Aleichem Street where Mr. Feldman's brother lived. The warmth and hospitality of this devout family had impressed Chava. They had an extra-special amount of kindness and devotion.

Then there was the surprise that Mr. Feldman's brother had achieved a miracle, and had found a two-bedroomed apartment to rent for his family. Their new friends, Mr. and Mrs. Feldman, had insisted the Bernsteins take one of the rooms until they could find other accommodation. Her parents had been overcome with gratitude. Her mother's eyes glistened with tears. Her father had said to the two Feldman families in a voice filled with emotion, "I hope one day I can find a way to repay you for your kindness."

So here they were. For the time being, they had a roof over their heads, and they were with people that Chava liked. Yet why did she feel so insecure, so terrified?

She heard Bashi cry and then stop. Then she heard her wailing loudly. It was an angry sobbing. She got up and knocked softly at the Feldmans' door. "Can I help you, Mrs. Feldman?" she whispered.

"Oh, thank you, my dear. It appears with all the excitement, I've lost my milk. If you'll just hold the baby for a few minutes, I'll make her a bottle." Mrs. Feldman made her way to the kitchen and Chava followed, Bashi in her arms.

When the bottle was ready, Chava said, "You look so tired, Mrs. Feldman and I can't sleep anyway. Let me feed Bashi and I'll put her down when she falls asleep."

"Oh, bless you Chava. Don't forget to pat her on the back to break the winds. And call me if she doesn't settle easily." A grateful Mrs. Feldman went back to bed.

In the kitchen, Chava watched as the tiny child drank from her bottle. For a second, she caught a glimpse of them both in a small mirror hung over the sink. She was surprised to find she looked the same as before she left Kovno. Her long, blonde hair was still thick and shiny. Her green eyes though troubled and intense, still sparkled despite her tiredness. She quickly turned her full lips upward into a smile - for Bashi's sake - and felt herself relax a little.

Bashi, wrapped in her warm blanket, was eagerly sucking from her bottle, her eyes puckered with concentration and effort. She drank quickly and hungrily. Chava patted her back and rocked her a little. She found herself enjoying the experience, maternal feelings aroused she had never been aware of before. Within a few minutes Bashi was satiated and sleeping. Chava peeked into the Feldmans' room and saw Mrs. Feldman, too, had fallen into a deep slumber. She tiptoed back to her own room and placed the baby carefully on the mattress next to her. With her arm around Bashi, she somehow felt comforted and finally drifted off to sleep.

In the morning light, things looked much better. It wasn't so bad to share a room with other people, Chava realised, as long as they were family. Her mother looked decidedly better after the rest. Her father said he was going to help his wife make their room a little more comfortable and then pay a visit to the bank.

Maish and Chava decided to explore the city. It was a day Chava never forgot. It was the day she suddenly realized how wonderful it was to have a big brother. Although in the past they had had their squabbles, today they were just happy to have each other for company. On the trolley car, Chava looked at him properly, taking note of his brown, wavy hair and brown eyes, his handsome smile and ruddy cheeks. "I do love him, this big brother of mine!" she said to herself.

When they reached the town, they spent some time looking at the sparkling sea. Drawn by its beauty, the two of them, who had seldom glimpsed any ocean, made their way past the imposing monument of the Duc de Richilieu. They ran down the Potjomkin Staircase and landed up paddling and picnicking at the Laungeron Beach which was within easy walking distance.

Chava was somehow aware she should appreciate these few hours she had with her older brother. She sensed he felt the same. He pointed out how the city curved like an amphitheatre along the coast of the Black Sea at a point where the high steppe of the Ukraine suddenly halted a hundred and fifty feet above sea level. She showed him the white acacias drooping in the summer heat.

They discussed their mutual concern about their mother's ill health. He spoke about his desire to enter the field of medical research, and she confessed to writing poetry. All too soon, they realized their parents would be concerned by their long absence. In a happy frame of mind, they made their way slowly up the staircase to head towards home.

When they reached the town, however, a strange sight awaited them. People were standing in groups, talking. Everybody seemed concerned, frightened. Fear gripping her heart, she made her way towards the one group and in her best Russian said, "Excuse me, but would you please tell me what has happened?"

An old man looked at them sadly. "War has broken out," he explained softly. "Hitler has attacked the Soviet Union."

"Lithuania?" Maish questioned. "Yes, my boy, Lithuania," came the reply.

Maish and Chava raced home as fast as they could, taking a taxi instead of a trolley car to avoid any delay. They noticed everybody else was doing the same - rushing home to share the terrible news with loved ones.

When they reached home, still harsher news awaited them. Sholem's voice trembled when he told his son that Stalin had ordered all men between the ages of eighteen and forty to register for the draft.

Maish digested this information for a minute. Then he said, "You warned me about this Pappa. If I must go, then let me go now, straight away."

That night, Chava began a letter to Rivka, wishing with all her heart that somehow or other the two friends could be closer to share their anxieties and feelings. She began the letter several times, each time wondering whether her emotional outpouring would upset Rivka and make her feel more distressed than necessary in the war situation in which she found herself. In the end, she wrote a simple, unemotional letter:

> *21 \ 4 Hospital Street*
> *Malanovka Section*
> *Odessa*
> *22nd June 1941*

My Dearest Rivki,

You must be surprised at our address. In the end, we could not make it all the way to Sverdlosk, and we have landed up staying with some lovely people, the Feldmans (also from Kovno), in Odessa. The Feldmans have two mischievous little boys and a sweet baby girl called Bashi that I adore.

I'm sure you think that our street has a strange name. Well, there is a hospital in this street. I learned from somebody today that a wealthy Jew called Gayevski built this hospital some time ago for poor Jews. Of course, today it is used by everyone.

Maish and I went for a lovely outing to the beach this morning. Along the way, we caught a glimpse of the city. It is very pretty - quite different to Kovno.

On the way back, we heard the terrible news that war has broken out. Maish has gone to register for the army and has been ordered to report for duty tomorrow.

I so much want you to know that I am thinking of you and your family and praying for your safety. Everyone here believes the Soviet soldiers will defeat the Germans and push them back very quickly. I hope they are right!

I miss you and hope that somehow or other, despite the war situation, this letter will reach you.

With fondest love,
Your friend, Chava

CHAPTER THREE

In later years, Chava could never tell exactly when she ceased to be a child and took on adult responsibilities. She only remembered it was in Odessa at the start of the war she learned to do housework and take care of little ones. It was then she learned to control tears that desperately needed to fall. And it was then she developed enough poise to walk into an army barracks full of whistling, teasing young men, determined to find her brother to give him the food parcels she and her mother had prepared.

On Friday 25th July, when Chava brought Maish a Sabbath *challa* and some savoury dishes she and her mother had lovingly prepared, he said to her, "Well, Chavale, looks like my holiday here is coming to an end. We leave by ship tomorrow night. Tell Pappa and Mamma to try to get down to the harbour tomorrow. Perhaps I'll have a chance to bid them farewell."

Late the next afternoon, with three huge army tankers looming over the huge crowd, Chava and her parents searched for hours among the thousands of soldiers and the local population, until they finally found Maish and managed to speak to him for a few minutes. His voice showed some pride and excitement aside from trepidation.

"Look!" he said. "This ship is called the Gruzia. It's going to hold seven thousand soldiers. The one at the back is called the Voroshilov. Six thousand will be on that one. And that smaller one in the middle is my ship. It's called the Lenin and I'll be one of three thousand."

Chava was taken aback when her father asked Maish if he would mind if he gave him the traditional Jewish blessing. Maish looked surprised. His parents didn't often practise Jewish customs and traditions.

Sholem cleared his throat and said, "Well, you know, when I left home, this is what my father gave to me and after all, it can't hurt." Then, with tears in his eyes and his outstretched hands placed gently on Maish's head, he blessed him. Chava and her parents each hugged Maish and a few minutes later he was gone.

But they all stayed at the harbour waiting for the ships to leave, waving goodbye to their Maish. As her eyes searched for her brother amongst the mass of cheerful young men, Chava tried to still a terrible feeling of dread that threatened to overwhelm her.

A few days later, when she returned from her shopping, she found her parents red-eyed and distraught, the Feldmans hovering over them. On her mother's bed lay a telegram which read: *We regret to inform you that your son, Moshe Elchanan Bernstein, has been reported as missing in action. His ship, the Lenin, was sunk in the harbour of Sebastopol in Crimea during the early hours of 30 July, 1941. Only two hundred and fifty men survived. Your son's name was not on the list of survivors.*

The feeling of dread Chava had carried around with her for days had gone. In its place were feelings of shock and grief. Her parents were unconsolable. She herself walked around in a daze, unable to fathom that her darling brother Maish was dead.

For seven days, the period of deep mourning, Mrs. Feldman insisted on bringing them food, although none of them had any appetite to eat. Mr. Feldman also organized a *minyan* in the evenings, a quorum of ten men, so that Sholem could say the Kaddish, the prayer of mourning for the dead. In the morning, he attended the synagogue to do the same.

Despite her griefstricken state, Chava was aware that Jewish refugees were pouring into the city from all over the Soviet Union, from places like Bukovina, Bessarabia and the Western Ukraine. It was strange how one way or another, all the refugees were taken care of. No-one starved or went without shelter. Once the first week of mourning was over, Chava went to offer her assistance with the refugees. It helped her to forget her own dreadful sorrow. It was also an escape from the woebegone face of her mother and the angry, tortured face of her father.

In the evenings, she would tell her parents about some of the more interesting families she had met during the day. She hoped her chatting would ease some of their pain. But when they went to bed, she would always hear one of them quietly sobbing. It was then she could no longer control herself. She would throw her face against the pillow, so that all sound was smothered, and weep in vast gulps.

The family were not given long to grieve, however. For soon, the worst happened. The Germans reached Odessa. The people of Odessa were faced with bombardment after bombardment, but spurred on by Stalin's exhortation not to give in, they refused to surrender. Like all the people of Odessa, the Bernsteins and the Feldmans lived in a state of constant anxiety and apprehension.

One late afternoon, just before the usual evening black-out, Sholem said to his daughter, "It's been a fairly quiet day, Chava, and Mamma's in a lot of pain. Please, run quickly to the hospital and get her medicine. It's still half an hour before the curfew, so you should have plenty of time. Only don't delay or we shall worry."

Looking at her mother's pain-racked face, Chava quickly put on her coat and sped off towards the hospital.   She had successfully obtained the medication and was on her way back home when an air attack began, specifically on Moldavanka. Chava was petrified. As she raced along the road, all she could hear was the thunder of the bombs, fire crackling and people screaming.

She didn't realize it, but she herself was screaming in sheer terror. She took shelter under some rubble for a little while and then, when it seemed the bombardments were moving to another part of the city, she made her way home through the ravaged street.

The apartment block in which she had lived with her family for the past weeks was semi-destroyed. Smoke filled her lungs as she raced to find her parents.

When she entered their room, she could see immediately her mother was dead. At first, she thought her father was dead, too, until she saw his lips moving. Quickly she made her way towards him, "Oh, Pappa, thank G-d you're alive!" she cried, taking his hand.

Her father gave an almost imperceptible shake of his head. Then he made a great effort. "Run!" he whispered. Chava put her arms around him and held him close. "Uzbekistan!" he rasped desperately. "Forgive me, Chavale!" He slumped back and closed his eyes.

Chava still hoped to save him. She ran to find some water, but the bathroom and kitchen were both in ruins and she could not find a functioning tap. She returned to her father. His eyes were still closed, so she took his hand, because in her head she was still his little girl and she needed his comforting strength. After a while, his hand became colder and colder, but she just sat there dazed, waiting for the sirens to cease their shrieking and the bombs to cease their thunder, and for help to come from somewhere.

Some time later, the sirens and bombing stopped. Chava was forced to shake herself out of her stupor when she heard a new sound - a baby's cry. "Oh, Bashi," she gasped. She made her way quickly next door. The room had been devastated. But in her cot, miraculously sheltered by a broken door lay Basha, the only one of her family left alive. Summoning up all her strength, Chava moved the heavy door and lifted out little Basha who was cold from shock and crying inconsolably.

Something happened to Chava then, something which forced her to push herself beyond her own terror and emotions. She changed Basha and dressed her warmly. She found a bottle of milk in the icebox, prepared by Mrs. Feldman for her baby. Basha drank, seemingly so hungry and thirsty she did not mind that the milk had not been warmed.

Chava wrapped Basha in a blanket and holding the baby in her arms, made her way to Sholem Aleichem Street, to where Mr. Feldman's brother lived. When she arrived, she didn't have to explain much. This was wartime. One minute your family was alive. The next minute, they were dead.

Basha's aunt took her out of Chava's arms. "Thank you, my dear, thank you for bringing her," the sad woman said. "And now, is there anything we can do for you?"

Chava thought of the couple's eight children - nine now that Basha had come. She considered asking them for a haven but then changed her mind. She did not want to add to the burden of this family. She had also had received definite instructions from her father.

"There is just one thing, please," she whispered. "When you bury Mr. and Mrs. Feldman and the boys, would you see to my parents, too?"

Mr. Feldman's brother was too heartbroken to speak. But he nodded vigorously. "Don't worry," his wife said, "we promise it will be done."

Still steeling herself against losing control, Chava went back to her apartment. Forcing herself not to look at the sights of death and horror in what had been her recent home, she packed a knapsack of clothes and a few other small possessions. Then she searched for her father's wallet which he kept inside a cupboard, placed it securely inside her clothes and went out.

Vaguely, she realized it was late, perhaps close to midnight. As if from afar, she watched as fire fighters extinguished fires and ambulancemen carried bodies, some dead and some alive, out of the ruins of houses and apartment buildings. She must have been standing watching the scene for about an hour as suddenly her legs felt weak and tired. Her cheeks burned slightly and there was a taste of salt in her mouth, indicating she had been crying. Her throat hurt, too, the result of heavy coughing spells throughout the night, brought on by the dense smoke.

In her weak, distraught state, she simply lay down on the side of the road and closed her eyes, to rest, to sleep, perhaps - she even hoped - to die. She slept that way until dawn, waking to the feeling of being gently prodded and to the sounds of two young people talking to each other in Yiddish.

" *'Zi iz teit.'* She's dead." a young male voice said.

" *'Nein, zi attemd noch. Zi lebt noch.'* No, she's still breathing, she's still alive," was the girlish reply.

Slowly she opened her eyes. Looking down at her were two teenagers. She could tell immediately they were religious Jews. The boy wore a cap and sidelocks, and despite the warm September air, the girl wore a long skirt and stockings.

"Can we help you?" the girl asked gently in Russian.

Chava didn't know how to reply. She wanted to ask for some warm, sweet tea. She knew she had to flee from Odessa, from the horror of war and destruction. Most of all, she needed friends.

In the end, all she could stammer was, " *'Mein Pappa hot mir gezokt ich muz gayen tzu Uzbekistan.'* My Pappa said I have to go to Uzbekistan." With an instinct that told her to make it known to them that she too was Jewish, she spoke in Yiddish.

"Come," the boy said. "We are also trying to reach Uzbekistan. Everyone is trying to flee to Uzbekistan or Kazhakstan, away from Odessa."

There was an undertone of agitation in his voice which persuaded Chava to stand up unsteadily and lift the knapsack which was at her side.

The two young people were both laden with baskets and knapsacks. With the sensitivity of one who had also experienced the horrors of war, the girl gave one of her lighter parcels to the boy and took Chava's hand. Together, they made their way down to the Odessa station.

They did not talk much along the way. With a sense of great urgency, they joined the running, panting throng of refugees making their way to the station, to leave Odessa for the Eastern Asiatic provinces of Russia. There they hoped to be far away from the battlefront and would enjoy a milder climate which would also improve their chances for survival.

In her grief and confusion, Chava sensed a source of strength and calm in the girl pulling her along by the hand and she was grateful. When they all stopped for a moment, to catch their breath and rearrange their 'luggage' the young girl said quickly, "My name is Devorah. I'm sixteen years old. And this is my brother Aharon. He's fourteen."

Chava nodded vaguely at them. "And I am Chava," she whispered softly.

A sight of total chaos awaited them at the station. Thousands of panic-stricken people were trying to leave Odessa. As it was wartime, all normal trains were being used by the army, so they had no alternative but to board a freight train overflowing with refugees. These trains were so overcrowded that everyone could scarcely breathe.

The inhuman conditions of the journey hardly bothered Chava, however. She was totally overwhelmed by grief. She was distraught about not remaining long enough in Odessa to be at her parents' burial. And she was terrified when she thought of a future alone in a foreign land.

It seemed, however, that her new-found friends were not going to abandon her. On a Thursday afternoon, when they had been travelling for a few days, Aharon told her they would be getting off at Voronezh, the next stop.

"It will be Shabbos tomorrow," he added. "Voronezh is quite a big town and there are bound to be Jews who will help us."

Chava became quite agitated. "But Aharon," she whimpered desperately, "it's important that we keep our places on the train, that we keep moving away from the fighting."

Devorah smiled calmly and gently put her arm around Chava. "Nothing is more important that the Shabbos, Chava. Nothing!" she answered quietly for her brother.

Chava could not bear the thought of being left alone. She had no alternative but to follow Devorah and Aharon as they sought out a kind religious family who took them in and shared the little they had.

In her distress and sorrow, she was vaguely aware that the hot food, the formal blessings and the tuneful melodies sung during the Sabbath meals all comforted her somewhat. If she had been able to break out of her personal darkness, she would have noticed the nervousness with which their hosts had taken them in. There was always the fear that such guests were spies on the lookout for 'religious zealots'.

She would also have noticed the joy that replaced the trepidation, when they discovered the depth of religious fervour and knowledge of two youngsters in a country that had, for decades, indoctrinated its people in atheist ideology.

On the Saturday evening, at the request of his host, Aharon gave a lesson on the Talmud to a group of men. They were all old. Some wept to hear a young man, a boy, expounding on Judaism, talking in phrases that reminded them of distant sounds of their childhood, on matters of which they had heard their fathers speak. And their fathers had learned in the great *yeshivot* of Eastern Europe, like Mir and Slabodka, all of which were no more.

Early the next morning, Chava and her companions again fought for places on a freight train heading south-east. As the time passed, Chava learned that Devorah and Aharon had five younger brothers and sisters, the youngest of whom was a tiny baby girl. Their mother had sent them ahead to find accommodation for the family before venturing on the long, difficult journey to Uzbekistan. When Chava asked about their father, they were rather reticent. All they would say was that he worked in Kiev and only came home occasionally.

On and on they travelled. As their train chugged slowly through Kazhakstan, the three youngsters noticed how the Russian landscape changed to vast stretches of desert, grasslands and mountains. The fact that they had now reached Asian territory was obvious. The dark complexion of the people, the desert robes of the men, the women who still wore their black shiny hair in long plaits, the teahouses and mosques of the cities all filled them with a sense of the Orient.

When they passed nomadic shepherds, who packed their felt-covered round huts onto their horses and travelled with the seasons, they could almost feel the land's exotic history of trade routes and camel trains, of outposts and cavalry, of Marco Polo and Genghis Khan.

Once they reached Uzbekistan, they began to see almond and fruit trees, cotton fields and many shepherds leading flocks of sheep. They passed the towns of Chelkor, Arelsk and Turkestan and finally arrived at their destination, Tashkent, the capital of Uzbekistan.

CHAPTER FOUR

Years later, when the war was finally over and Chava was back in Odessa, she wrote the following letter to her old friend Rivka of Kovno:

> *24/6 Rozumovsky Boulevard*
> *Odessa*
> *28th July 1945*

My dear Rivki,

The war has finally ended and we are aware of the great catastrophes that befell the Jews in the occupied territories - millions have perished! Yet I have a strange feeling in my heart you are still alive. It is because of this conviction that I wanted to write to you, to tell you firstly, thank G-d, I am alive, and also to share with you, my childhood friend, my life and experiences during these terrible war years.

I don't know whether you ever received a letter I wrote to you during the first weeks of the war, in which I told you that in the end we did not go all the way to Sverdlovsk, but landed up, instead, in Odessa. It was there we learned of the death of my dear brother Maish, on an army tanker called the Lenin. A few weeks later, my beloved parents were killed during one of the bombardments of Odessa.

I was saved from total desolation by two wonderful people, Devorah Levy and her brother Aharon. It was with them that I travelled as a war-time refugee down to Uzbekistan, and together we stayed and survived the war.

Our first stop in Uzbekistan was in the capital. All I can remember, now, of our brief stay in Tashkent are the long, slow queues at the Evapunkt, the government offices established to attend to the needs of the huge onslaught of refugees. These facilities were not nearly adequate for the relief work required. It was virtually impossible to find housing, jobs or even food. We slept in a broken-down hut which we shared with eight other people. Tashkent itself was in the grip of famine, and at the start of the winter it was hard to find a loaf of bread. We began to be plagued by real hunger then and we knew we would have to move on.

Devorah and Aharon kept introducing themselves to all the Jews they met so that among those who remained in Tashkent, there would be someone who could report their whereabouts. Let me tell you a little bit about the Jews we found when we came to Uzbekistan. Firstly, there were the Bukharan Jews who, I'm sure you know, have lived in Uzbekistan for many generations. They all spoke a Tajiki-Jewish dialect none of the Russian Jews could understand. Their children, however, who attended school with the rest of the population, were able to communicate in Russian.

There were also some Russian Jews who had been in Uzbekistan for a few years. During Stalin's purges of the 1930s, they had been accused of crimes such as Zionism and Socialism and had been sent to labour camps or to exile in Siberia. On their release, they had decided to move to Uzbekistan, which they regarded as somewhat 'safer' than Moscow or Kiev. And then, of course, there were thousands of Jews like Devorah, Aharon and me, who were fleeing from the Germans.

After much discussion, we decided to move on to Samarkand, the second largest city of Uzbekistan. By this time, Devorah and Aharon had run out of money. I was grateful to still have a little something left in my Pappa's wallet so I was at long last able to assist my two friends and benefactors.

In Samarkand, we were more fortunate. Although a large section of the town lived in very primitive conditions, we managed to acquire our own little two-bedroomed apartment where we found some comfort and warmth. Devorah and I began to work in a factory which made trousers for the soldiers in the army, and I enrolled at an evening college so I could finish my schooling. Aharon was rejected by all the factories as being 'too young', so he began to mend watches, a skill his father had taught him.

One evening, a few weeks after we had settled in Samarkand, I was sitting and mending our clothes. I looked at Devorah, who was busy at the sink washing the supper dishes. As usual, her dark hair was in one long plait down her back, her cheeks were red from the warmth of the oven, her brown eyes sparkled. A half-smile played around her lips as she hummed a well-known melody.

Then I looked at Aharon who was hunched over his religious books. He looked like a typical adolescent - his arms and legs were a little too long for his body. His yarmulka had slipped to the front of his head. He chanted quietly, although this chanting was different to the singing of his sister. Devorah was humming absent-mindedly but he was concentrating intensely. He was learning Torah.

My quiet reverie was interrupted by a noise outside the apartment. A man's voice said, "Excuse me, can you tell me where I can find Devorah and Aharon Levy?"

I heard our neighbour reply, "You're right there, comrade, I'm sure you'll find them home."

Devorah shouted, "Tatteh!" and I saw both her and Aharon fly to the door. A second later all was confusion and happiness. Uncle Dov, Devorah and Aharon's father, had arrived. He told us that, on his return from Kiev, he had tried to enter Odessa, but the city was under siege. So he decided to make his way to Uzbekistan where he hoped to find Devorah and Aharon... and he did!

What joy there was in our little home that day! What a great and special man he was, Rivki! He was part of a secret underground movement that taught Torah to young Jewish children. I finally understood why Devorah and Aharon had not wished to disclose any information about him. Before the war, anyone seen trying to keep mitzvos or teach Torah would be accused of some trumped-up charge and tortured to death or sent into exile where they were seldom heard of again.

He would spend hours explaining different Jewish laws and concepts to me. Thanks to him, Devorah and Aharon, I learned a deep understanding of Judaism. Later I knew clearly why Uncle Dov had dedicated his life to the secret teaching of Torah.

Lithuania had become a part of the Soviet Union just before the Second World War, so you and I didn't realise how, soon after the Revolution in Russia, those who took control of the Soviet government tried every possible means of stamping out Judaism.

This whole terrible exercise seemed to be ten times worse than the persecutions of the Jews by Alexander the Great. And they almost succeeded in their mission. In fact. I think they would have, if not for people like my dear friends who were totally dedicated to Torah and totally uncompromising in their practice of mitzvos.

You are probably wondering what happened to the rest of the family - the mother and little children who were left in Odessa. Sadly, I was never privileged to meet them. All the Jewish refugees in Samarkand were quite unaware of what was happening to their families in the occupied territory during the war, until Shavuos of 1943, when a stranger, a general who had taken leave of absence from the battlefront, came into our shul *in Samarkand. He had come to say Kaddish. All the Jews in that little Shul were East European Jews who had family and friends in Russia. They all came rushing up to ask what was happening at the front.*

"We're advancing," he said. "We're pushing the Germans back."

"How did the Jews fare in those parts?" everyone wanted to know.

He stared at them and then told them slowly, "There are no Jews anywhere, my friends. Don't you know that the Nazis hunted them down and killed every single one? Millions of Jews were murdered. Don't hope to find a single relative alive! I'm saying Kaddish now, Kaddish for two million Jews!"

You can imagine how shattered we all were, especially Uncle Dov, Devorah and Aharon. I know that deep in their hearts, all three secretly hoped that despite everything, they would later find the family intact or at least one member of the family still alive. But when Odessa was liberated in April last year, there was no trace of them. Of all the eighty to ninety thousand Jews who had lived in Odessa before the war, only a few thousand had survived.

The Germans used all the methods they used in every town of Europe to make it Judenrein. Massacres by shooting, massacres by burning, mass deportations and forced marches to camps where they died of disease or hunger or cold or more massacres. The Germans were helped by Rumanian soldiers, part of the invading army, and also by the Ukrainian militia.

I am not going to dwell on this. I am sure you know better than me the horrors to which our people were subjected. Of course, we all lived in the shadow of unspeakable sorrow, but nevertheless we carried on, aware that compared to many, many others, we were fortunate.

Uncle Dov and Aharon together made a small income from their watchmaking. They also saw to many of the communal needs of the Jewish refugees. Thanks to them, there was a minyan *at our small apartment every Friday night and Saturday. They found a* shochet *for the occasional chicken someone managed to buy. They were always happy to teach Torah or Talmud to whoever asked to learn. They considered this to be an honour and would never charge for their services.*

You're probably wondering how a young chap like Aharon had such a vast knowledge at his age. Uncle Dov once explained to me that he was always afraid he would be picked up suddenly by the Soviet police and he would die without having passed his knowledge on to his children. There were very few people in Russia who were knowledgeable in Jewish matters, even fewer who would risk their lives by teaching. So from the time Aharon was three years old, Uncle Dov would sit and teach him every day. This of course applied to all his children, but Aharon seemed to have a special gift for learning and had the ability to spend hours in Torah study from a young age.

Devorah and I worked, of course, in the factory which made trousers for the soldiers in the army. How strange it was for me Rivki! You remember how life was in Kovno before the war? We were really quite spoiled then, going to school every day and pulling a face if our mothers asked us to wash the floors or help in the kitchen! My life changed so suddenly and so drastically, I scarcely knew who I was!

While one could never call it a normal life, the days did take on a form, a pattern, despite the war we knew was raging close by and the daily struggle for enough food to fill our bellies.

We did have friends, though. After a while, we came to realize there were quite a few Chassidic families in the town - not as many as there were in Tashkent - but enough to feel we were not alone. We all helped each other. Poor Uncle Dov, Devorah and Aharon had to fight terrible inner feelings of guilt and grief and a lot of other people were suffering in the same way.

Of course, there were many Misnagdim. And then there were the Bukharan Jews. I made friends with a Bukharan girl I met at work. Quite often, I'd visit her home where her mother, dressed in a long loose blouse and pantaloons, would be cooking her dumplings, pilaff and bread on the earthen floor of her open kitchen.

Early last year, when we could see the war would soon be over, a young man came to learn with Uncle Dov. He had been drafted into the army right at the beginning of the war and had been badly injured almost immediately, leaving him with a slight limp. As a result, the army released him from duty. I could tell immediately he was not a Chassid by the way he dressed and cut his beard. We eyed each other secretly and I rather liked the look of him.

When I asked about him, Uncle Dov told me that he came from Odessa. His Russian name was

*Alexander, but he liked to be called by his Hebrew
name, Asher. When I continued to ask about him,
Uncle Dov looked at me very keenly and said , "I think
you should ask him yourself!"*

*Sure enough, the next day, after their studies,
Uncle Dov called me and said Asher would like to take
a walk with me. That was the first of many walks we
took together.*

*I told him I was born in Kovno. My parents had
not been particularly religious, but had sent me to a
Jewish Day School until the Russians occupied
Lithuania in 1940. I told him how I used to love to
spend Shabbos and other festive meals at your home
because there I always felt a true Torah atmosphere.
And I told him how I had fled with my family to
Odessa and what tragedies had befallen us there.*

*When we heard the war was over, Asher asked
Uncle Dov's permission to marry me. I was only
eighteen at the time, and as Uncle Dov had become a
father to me, it was only right that his permission be
asked.*

*I asked Uncle Dov if he minded that Asher was a
Misnaged and not a Chassid, and he laughed and
said, "Ribbono Shel Olam! Whatever for? He's a good
Torah loving Jew and you have become a devout
Jewess. I'm sure you are going to be very happy
together. Besides, being a Litvak, you probably come
from a family of staunch Misnagdim yourself!"*

*We were married by Uncle Dov in a very simple but
happy ceremony. Devorah was my bridesmaid. She
had also found a* shidduch, *but she wanted to get
married in Odessa. She hoped she might still find her
mother alive to witness her wedding. She and her
fiance, Chaim Gutstein, intended to live in Odessa
anyway.*

Uncle Dov wanted to go back and look for his wife, children and other family members. Asher wanted to return and search for his family, and I said I would be happy as long as I was with Asher and close to my dear friend, Devorah. So, soon after the war ended, we all packed up and went back to Odessa.

Who knows if it was a good decision or not? Only time will tell. In the meantime, I, thank G-d, am happy. Asher is a kind and loving husband. (I think he is handsome,too!) He promised not to take me back to Moldavanka, which held terrible memories of the war for me.

We are most fortunate to have found a little apartment in Rozumovsky Boulevard, in the part of the city that was the business area of the Jewish merchants before the war. The area is quite run down, but the apartment is comfortable and contains two small living rooms aside from the kitchen, so I feel like a queen.

Asher has found work at a textile factory which has a five-day week from Monday to Friday. What a relief not to have to explain about Shabbos! As soon as I am a little more settled, I, too, will look for work.

In desperation, I am writing to you at your old address in Kovno. I feel a little silly. Who knows whether you are alive, let alone still living in Kovno! And yet it has been wonderful to unburden myself to an old friend, regardless of whether you will receive this letter or not. If by some strange good fortune you do receive this letter, please reply and tell me about yourself.

> *Your loving friend,*
> *Chava*

CHAPTER FIVE

Asher came home just as Chava was finishing her letter. She greeted her new husband warmly and offered him some tea.

"You look happy, Chavale," Asher remarked, "did anything exciting happen today?"

Chava knew how much he was longing to have children. She, too, waited anxiously each month, hoping that she had finally been blessed with a pregnancy, only to be bitterly disappointed. The doctors said there was no medical problem. They just had to be patient.

She swallowed hard. "Not really, Asherel. I know you'll think me a little silly," she replied, "but I wrote a letter to an old friend of mine from Kovno, telling her how we spent the war years and about the wonderful man I married. You know, just catching up on five years and asking about her life."

As she saw Asher open his mouth to protest, she added quickly, "Oh, I know she probably isn't alive anymore. Even if she is, she's probably gone off to Palestine or America, but I thought I would try anyway. Perhaps, somehow, she left a forwarding address at the Post Office. Or perhaps the neighbours have her details and will pass the letter on. Rivka would be so happy to hear I've become observant and have even married somebody who is *frum*."

"I hope you didn't write about the Levys, Chava. I hope you didn't go into any details."

"Oh, Asher, I know you've told me you had a terrible childhood, that there have been times of great oppression and antisemitism. But now all the Soviet people have seen the results of rabid antisemitism. The Yiddish newspapers are talking about six million Jews in Europe. Surely they've learned something from that! Besides, you know there's been an easing up during the war years. We're all talking about reopening a Yiddish day school. They're allowing publications in Yiddish. It's finished now, Asherel. You must try to put the past behind you, and not be too fearful."

She handed him his tea. He placed it on the table to cool and sat down. Chava just watched him lovingly. She couldn't help but notice his curly, black hair and brown eyes, his olive complexion and lips that usually smiled at her, except that now, Asher was frowning. "Oh, why can't he let go of the past?" she thought to herself.

Asher considered deeply for a few minutes and then came to a decision. "Chavale," he began with a sigh. "Do you know what Chaim told me just the other day? He said that Aharon had written to them from Kiev, telling them there was recently a pogrom in Kiev in which several Jews lost their lives. Even in Kielce in Poland, I believe, when a few broken Jews came back from the camps and tried to re-establish themselves in their homes, they were murdered by their old neighbours who still thirsted for blood."

Chava shivered. Odessa was not far from Kiev.

Asher continued, "I didn't want to talk to you about this and upset you. What is important about these pogroms is that, as before, a few more Jews have been killed and no-one has been brought to justice."

"I think you must tell me about the Soviet Union, Asherel." Chava said quietly. "Whenever I've asked you to talk about your childhood in Odessa, you've said 'Some other time. Not now.' So, I'm telling you, now's the time. If I'm going to live here in Odessa, I have to know, I have to understand what I'm dealing with."

She brought her cup of tea to the kitchen table and sat down opposite Asher.

Again he sighed deeply and then began to speak with great difficulty. "All right," he said, "let me think where to start. I think I mentioned to you before, my family originally came from Kishinev, close by. My father was a rabbi. My mother always told me that he was known for his piety and acts of loving kindness, and she, too, came from a family of learning and piety. They were married in 1912 and I was the seventh and last child born to them. My family apparently lived quite happily until 1917 when the Russian Revolution took place.

"Everybody knows what happened in the Ukraine after the Revolution. Some Ukrainians didn't want to secede to Russia and some did. A ghastly civil war began - a clashing of wild mobs of warring soldiers, seeking loot and bloodshed."

He gave a wry smile. "You know how people think. For the communists, every Jew was a capitalist, a factory owner or rich merchant, a member of the hated bourgeoisie. For the nationalists, every Jew was a communist, walking around talking about a new era of equality and justice for all, explaining to others the wonderful ideology of Karl Marx, the Jew.

"Both views were good excuses for antisemitism. For the next five years, the most terrible pogroms took place in the Ukraine. Approximately a hundred and fifty thousand Jews were massacred."

Chava shook her head sadly. "So many?" she said. "I didn't know. My parents spoke about it, but I don't think they realized how many people were involved."

"Of course," Asher went on, "the communists eventually defeated the Ukrainians.

"I was born in 1922, just about the time when the communists took over. The Jews hoped it would bring a measure of calm and stability to this region, and it did. Then a different kind of torment began. As you know, the communists did everything in their power to spread their philosophy.

"They couldn't tolerate religion, feeling that religious beliefs were a continuing source of hatred and political dissension against Communism. In their view, there could never be unity as long as destructive religious forces were rife. To convince the masses, they said 'Religion teaches that some people have to be poor and others rich, that people must accept their suffering. This is only a subterfuge to suppress all the workers. Religion is the opium of the masses!'

"As soon as the communists seized power, they began a campaign against all religion. For us Jews, this meant the banning of all Jewish organizations, religious and non-religious. At the same time, anyone willing to follow the communist line was appointed to a respected position and publicly honoured.

"Some Jews, who had already distanced themselves from a Torah way of life decided to join the Communist Party. They were taken in by Lenin's promise of equality for the Jews. They felt they could maintain their Jewish identity and still be accepted by the communists if they went along with their philosophy. People like that landed up forming the nucleus of the infamous Yevsektzia, a government organization, consisting mainly of Jews, whose task it was to indoctrinate the Jewish people in Party ideals."

Chava was listening intently. "How could that be?" she asked.

"Well," Asher explained, "the Yevsektzia was probably the most powerful tool the communists had to destroy the faith of the Jewish people. Before long, there were branches of the Yevsektzia in every town and village.

"They acted with lightning speed. *Chadarim* and *yeshivot* were immediately closed. New government schools were opened. The teachers there were Jews who were happy to spread communist ideals. Such people also headed the local Jewish councils. Hebrew books could no longer be published. Our Yiddish periodicals, some of which had a readership of hundreds of thousands, were banned.

"All we had to read were blatantly anti-religious and anti-Zionist magazines and newspapers. I remember one magazine called 'Apikores', Heretic. It had a cover with a picture of a spear piercing a small circle containing a bearded religious Jew and a Star of David.

"The first people to be attacked were the heads of *yeshivot*, rabbis, *cheder* teachers and religious community leaders. The Yevsektzia would find ways of slandering them and once the victims were brought to court, their fate was clear. Some rabbis were imprisoned and tortured, others were transported to Siberia and not heard from again."

Asher cupped his face with his right hand and screwed up his eyes. "My father was such a victim."

he continued. "He was caught teaching a group of Barmitzvah boys how to lay *tefillin*. He was put on trial for 'spreading anti-Soviet propaganda', imprisoned and tortured to death. I was just a baby at the time. My older brother, Ya'acov, and my sisters had a little time to benefit from all my father taught them, and of course, from his love. They'd had time to learn from both my parents before the decrees began."

Chava remained silent, although her eyes were bright with tears. "At least I had my Pappa until I was fourteen years old. I should consider myself fortunate," she thought to herself.

Now Asher had begun, he couldn't stop the flow of memories. "My poor mother didn't know what to do about her children's education. She wanted to keep us at home and have us taught there. But few people were willing to risk imprisonment or worse by teaching Torah. Besides, there were strict laws. Parents who didn't send their children to the new schools were fined. If they persisted, they were put on trial and received a harsh punishment. In the end, nearly everyone sent their children to the government schools, except for those who were brave enough to endanger their entire family.

"And what schools they were! Rather call them institutions of indoctrination! Although the special schools for Jewish children provided lessons in Yiddish, it was clear that no religious studies were going to be taught there. The purpose of these schools was to infuse communism among the Jewish population. Even children from religious families soon came to mock the *mitzvot* carried out by their parents and grandparents.

"Some Jews, like my mother, decided to send their children to gentile schools where Christianity was denigrated rather than Judaism.

"Every day, the teacher would call out 'Is there a G-d?' and we would all have to reply in unison, 'No!'

"Or the teacher would say 'Let's all say 'G-d, give us candy!' The children would all call out this request in unison. 'Well, did anyone get candy?' the teacher would ask. 'No!' all the children would shout.

"'Now let's say 'Lenin, give us candy'. The children would obey her and very quickly a bag of candy would be brought in."

"Oh, you must be exaggerating," Chava exclaimed.

"No, I'm not," Asher replied. "You wouldn't believe to what lengths the Soviet government went in order to stamp out religion. One of their first tricks was to institute a new calendar. A week was changed to six days instead of seven. Schools and factories were open five days and closed on the sixth. So Jewish children who were forced to attend school, would transgress five out of every six Sabbaths. Even on the 'rest day', adults and older children were expected to volunteer their assistance in the fields and factories.

"We suffered terribly over this period, Chava. You, at least, had a sweet, calm childhood, thank G-d. My childhood was one of upheaval, hunger and fear.

"The government took factories from their owners, a large percentage of whom were Jewish. Many Jews began to work in these factories as it was the only way for them to make a living. Each factory had a party secretary who observed the workers closely. So the Ministry of the Interior, which later became the N.K.V.D., eventually had a file on everyone.

"My brother, Ya'acov, who worked in a ship building factory, was constantly hounded by the Yevesektzia, for staying away on Shabbos and for not eating the unkosher lunches the factory provided. Eventually, he lost his job. He could not find any other work that would accept someone who would not work on Shabbos. When he was eighteen, he was arrested for being a 'parasite' - people who did not want to work - and sent to Siberia. We never heard from him again. A few months after his arrest, my mother received a letter informing her of his death.

"I was only five years old at the time, but I remember clearly the terrible sadness of my mother. When my father was taken from her, she still maintained her strength for the sake of her children. After Ya'acov was taken, she was emotionally destroyed. She was left with me and my three sisters, who were all much older than me.

"The authorities had expropriated farmland belonging to the *kulaks* - land owners. They then created *kolkhozes*, communal farms where people worked for a fixed salary. My Mamma decided to send my sisters to work on one of the nearby *kolkhozes*, so they would be able to support themselves.

"Disaster struck very soon after that. Government officials came without warning and took away the produce of the *kolkhozes* - fruit, vegetables, geese and cattle. All the goods plundered were put on to freight trains and sent to the north. A time of terrible famine began in the Ukraine. Millions of people died of hunger in one winter. The people hardest hit were those who lived in the country and the smaller villages.

"In Odessa, where I lived with my Mamma, food was a most expensive commodity. Mamma made a few kopeks out of teaching children in secret how to *daven* from a *siddur*, but having a little money did not help much. No food was available. Eventually, when both of us were starving and our bodies swollen from hunger, Mamma sold her silver candlesticks for a little bread. My sisters, thank goodness, were more fortunate. Every *kolkhoz* had a cafeteria where food was given to the workers. So they, at least, were not too hungry. They even smuggled some of their food out to us when they could.

"Of course, the government thought of new ideas. They opened up small shops where food was sold for foreign currency and precious metals. When they felt they weren't making enough, they asked members of the Yevsektsia to tell them who the wealthy Jews were. They were arrested at night and tortured, until they revealed their 'hidden treasures'.

"Not only did they imprison the wealthy, but anyone who did not adhere to their views. Newspapers made impassioned cries against the 'enemies of the people', the counter-revolutionaries who, they claimed, were planning an uprising with forces outside the country. Anyone deviating from the party line was accused of issuing propaganda against them. People were encouraged to inform on others, even if they were friends or family. Many people did so in order to prove their loyalty to the communists. It was also an easy way to destroy one's personal enemies."

Asher suddenly gave a wry smile, "You know, Chava, informing on others became so rife that there was a joke that people used to tell : A man looked in the mirror and said to his reflection, 'Tell me, which one is the informer, me or you?' "

But now, Chava noticed, Asher's face had clouded over once again, as he went on, "In later years, when Stalin's purges began, among all the others who went to their deaths were many members of the Yevesektzia who shared the same fate of their victims a decade before.

"At the same time, there was another famine in Odessa. Every day was a torment of hunger and fear. Life had become so bad for the Jews that *shochtim* were afraid to *shecht, mohelim* were afraid to perform circumcisions and *chazanim* were afraid to *daven. Shuls* and *minyanim* were prohibited. There were those who formed *minyanim* in their homes and paid for it with their lives. Religious people were put into a position of being forced to flee to a neighbouring country, such as Poland, which was an extremely difficult and dangerous undertaking, or live in a constant state of fear."

"And you, Asherel?" Chava asked gently.

"I was one of the great successes of the government campaign of indoctrination and terror. I grew up as a non-believer. Even when my mother and sisters would attend a secret *minyan* on the evening of Yom Kippur, I would wait at home, not even wanting to learn how to pray. Oh, of course I would always try to show my mother respect. She kept Kashrut at home and would try to show us when it was Shabbos. The candles were lit. A clean white cloth was on the table.

"There's one memory I have of my mother which has always been with me. She often used to beg me to let her show me how to *daven* and I always refused. Once, when she was really pleading with me on this matter, I laughed and said, 'What do you ask of G-d when you pray?'

"When she replied she had tears in her eyes. 'I beg G-d to keep my daughters Jewish and to give my son understanding so that one day, he, too, will turn back to the ways of the Torah'.

"Well, I suppose her prayers were answered, Chava. All three of my sisters married Jewish men and tried to keep the *mitzvot* as best as they could. I only wish my mother were alive to see me today. When I was in Tashkent, I thought of her and also about my brother Ya'acov's love of Torah. I wanted to find out more about Judaism before finally making the decision to discard it.

"It's an absolute miracle that I landed up at a place where there was a whole underground network of *chadarim*, set up by the wonderful Rabbi Chazan. The teachers were elderly men who were devoted to their students and who tried to imbue them with a love for Judaism. They taught Torah on all levels, from the Aleph Beis and reading in the Siddur, to studying Gemarah. Can you imagine a whole operation like that taking place in secret? Thanks to dedicated Chassidim like those in Tashkent and Uncle Dov, Devorah and Aharon, you and I learned about Torah and became observant."

Asher stopped suddenly. "Chava, what are you doing?"

Chava was standing at the stove and tearing her letter to Rivka into little pieces. "I'm burning this letter. You've made me feel afraid. I don't want to take any chances. Rivka probably isn't alive, anyway."

That night, as they lay beside each other in the darkness, tears flowed down Chava's cheeks. "Why are you crying, my darling?" Asher asked.

Chava's reply came from the depths of her breaking heart. "I just wish your mother and my parents were alive to see us now. They would have been so happy for us and so proud. If only we had found one member of our close family with whom we could share our lives!"

CHAPTER SIX

A few weeks later on a warm August evening, Asher and Chava were preparing to go out. Devorah had confided to Chava that she was pregnant with her first child and not feeling very well. It was for this reason that Chava had made the suggestion they visit their friends.

Just as Chava was putting on her scarf, the doorbell suddenly rang loudly and urgently. Asher seemed apprehensive. Gently, he held Chava back and said quietly, "Let me answer the door, Chava."

He cautiously opened the door only to be confronted by a thin, somewhat harassed-looking woman. Clutching her hand was a small dark-haired boy who reminded Asher of someone he could not place.

"Excuse me," said the woman. "Is this the home of Asher Aharonowitz?"

"Yes, it is," Asher replied. "How can I help you? Please come in."

The woman entered the living room slowly. She looked around her as if trying to survey and sum up her surroundings all at once.

"Do sit down," Chava said. "Can we bring you some tea and some juice for your little boy?"

"Yes, that would be nice," she replied.

In the kitchen, as Asher and Chava prepared the glasses of tea and juice, they raised their eyes questioningly at each other.

"Did we meet this child in Samarkand?" Asher whispered to Chava. "He looks so familiar to me."

Chava shook her head. "Not to me," she whispered back. "But his dark, curly hair looks a little like yours!"

They smiled at each other as Chava carried the tray and they both re-entered the living room. Chava noticed that the woman was still surveying the room carefully. She was a little annoyed. What did this woman want?

As the woman and the little boy extended their arms, Chava suddenly noticed their tattooed numbers and a shiver of shock went through her. It was the first time they had been so close to survivors of the camps. They had heard about it, of course, but still, seeing those numbers horrified them.

The little boy gulped down his drink without raising his eyes and without speaking.

"My name is Freida, Freida Gershon," the woman began. "During the war, I was in a camp in Berezovka. I shared a barracks with a certain woman called Leah Rivkin, whose maiden name was Aharonowitz."

Asher suddenly sat down. He looked deathly pale. "That's my sister," he said.

"I thought so," the woman said. "I am sorry to tell you she died of typhus just before the war ended, leaving behind her only son, this little boy, Yossel."

Asher put his hands to his face as if recovering from a blow. He had searched all the records and found no indication that any members of his family were alive. Still, having his sister's death reported to him so plainly, left him shocked and upset.

Speechless, Chava gazed at the boy, who remained silent and passive throughout the conversation.

Freida stumbled on quickly. "Knowing she was about to die, Leah made me write down the names of all the members of her family, so there would be someone to look after the boy. I have searched very hard and you, Asher, are the only one I have found alive."

Asher, too, was now staring at the little boy, tears in his eyes.

"Although she was very weak during her last few days," Freida continued, "Leah kept repeating that if Yossel would end up staying with you, I was to beg you to get him a teacher so he could learn about Judaism. I see now she was rambling on irrationally. She seemed to think you had no interest in religious matters." The visitor looked pointedly at the Sabbath candlesticks on the table and Asher's Gemorah volumes stacked on top of the bookcase.

"No, what she said to you was perfectly sound," Asher said quietly. "She remembered me as I was before the war. I've changed."

"What a *mazal!*" the woman exclaimed. "She so wanted the boy to have a proper Jewish upbringing. And after all we've been through, how many of us today can provide that for the children? I've come here to ask you to consider whether you can take the boy in. I was left a widow, you see," the woman continued quickly, "and now I hope to remarry. This man has two children of his own whom he hopes I will help to bring up. You know how hard it is for a woman having to work, do all the housework and raise the children. And poor Yossel, here, is... well, in some ways so easy, but in other ways so difficult. Unfortunately, he cannot speak. Of course, we could always go to the authorities. They say that nowadays the orphanages are in much better condition than..."

"No!" Asher and Chava both shouted in unison. Then they just stared at each other. They had both fallen in love with the dark, curly-haired, silent little boy who sat with them.

"Well, if you both feel that way, then of course there's no problem," said Freida, sounding relieved. "I promised Leah, you see, and with me, a promise is a promise. Before I went through the war, I still used to say some prayers my Mama had taught me, despite Stalin. Now I don't believe in anything anymore. If there is a G-d somewhere, He took my parents, my husband and my children, and I won't speak to a G-d Who forsakes his people to such an extent. I'm marrying a gentile man who is kind and good. That's war for you. Some find G-d, some lose G-d. But still, a promise is a promise."

"We'll take him," said Asher, looking at Chava pleadingly. "We'll take him right away."

Chava nodded slowly in agreement, a hundred strange thoughts racing through her head. "How does one take care of a little boy? I don't really know anything about babies and children. And he's mute. How does one communicate with someone who doesn't speak?"

"H...has Yossel always been this way?" she asked hesitantly.

"His mother said no. His mother said he was born on the 15th September 1941 during the heavy bombing of Odessa. She said he was perfectly normal until the age of two and a half, despite the terrible conditions of his life. Then he witnessed seven people being shot in front of him, and he never spoke again. How she fought, your sister Leah, to keep this child alive. In a way, it was better for her that the child didn't speak, didn't even cry much. It was easier that way to keep him from harm."

Chava had the feeling that Freida could have gone on and on, and she wasn't brave enough to hear all she had to say. She didn't want to hear how Freida's children had died. And, for some strange reason she did not understand, she already felt protective of Yossel. He had been through the unbearable and she did not want him to relive the horrors of his life through words.

"But does he understand what people say to him?" she asked.

"Yossel understands perfectly," Freida replied. "He understands Yiddish, Russian and German." There was a note of pride in her voice. "Sometimes he would overhear conversations between the German or Russian guards. He would run quickly to his mother and warn her in his own mute way if danger was imminent. He was a little spy for our whole barracks. Once he..."

Again Chava had the feeling that her guest wished to ramble on. She quickly interrupted. "When can we fetch his clothes?"

"I brought them with me. My fiance is outside in the car, waiting for me. He has them," she said.

"Then I will go down and fetch them," said Asher as he strode towards the door.

While Asher was out, Chava tried to find out more about the little boy who would soon be in their care. "Is there anything special Yossel likes to eat?" she asked.

Freida gave a little chuckle. "A camp child? A child who has been in the camps is happy to have any food to eat. Be careful, though, not to give him any rich food. People like us who have been deprived of eggs and milk, find it hard to stomach red meat and cream."

She suddenly became agitated, glancing again and again at Yossel. Then resolutely she rose, sat on the floor in front of Yossel and taking his head in her hands said in a broken voice in Yiddish, "You remember, Yossel. I've explained it to you. It was your Mamma's wish that you should grow up with her family. And we found your family, your Uncle Asher and his wife, your Aunt. You are a good boy, a good boy. I will miss you and I will come to see you often." There were tears in her eyes.

She stood up abruptly as Asher entered the room with a small bundle, and immediately began to walk towards the door. "A promise is a promise," Chava heard her repeating to herself. As she reached the door, she stopped for a few seconds. "I will come to visit soon," she said, first looking at Chava and Asher, and then at Yossel, "soon."

Yossel did not cry and he did not cling to his foster mother. His eyes showed understanding and also pain. He stood very still and swallowed hard. Chava felt herself ache for him, for all he had known and lost.

Asher made tea and poured a glass of milk for Yossel. Chava went to fetch a cake she had prepared for the next day, for Shabbos. The boy drank the milk and ate his piece of cake. Chava wondered whether he needed time alone to grieve for the loss of Freida and to reconcile himself to his new circumstances. When he was settled on the sofa in the living room, she did not stay with him, fighting her own need to comfort this child. "If it were me," she thought to herself, "I'd want to weep - alone."

Later when she went to check on him, she saw that he had fallen asleep, but there were tear-stains on his cheeks. That night, when Chava and Asher finally fell asleep after hours of whispering to each other and coming to terms with their changed situation Chava woke up and found tears streaming down her face. Asher, who was not sleeping well either, asked, "Did you have a bad dream?"

"Yes," she replied. "I dreamed about Bashi."

"Bashi? Who's Bashi?"

"A little baby girl I held in my arms a few times when the war started. I don't think she's alive. I don't think she could have made it through the war."

Asher took Chava in his arms to comfort her, and together they waited for the dawn.

CHAPTER SEVEN

The next few months were difficult for Chava and Asher. They were both young and inexperienced at the job of parenting. Little Yossel, who had lost his father, mother and siblings and then had to bid farewell to his foster mother, was silent and withdrawn. How were they to deal with this small "old man" who had been in hell and showed no wish to rejoin the world where he might be hurt and abandoned yet again?

Left alone with him for most of the day, Chava fed him, washed him and tried desperately to reach him, to draw him back into the world. She feared that if she and Asher did not succeed, they would have to approach the medical authorities, who with their white coats and syringes, might end any possibility of Yossel's leading a normal life forever.

And so she followed her heart and her instincts, trying to put herself in Yossel's mind, trying to work out how she might be comforted if she had experienced the same horrors. She read to Yossel - stories that were neither too sad nor violent. They joined the library, and Yossel seemed to enjoy visiting the modern, grey building with its quiet atmosphere and abundant rows of books. The outing seemed to be one in which he could find some sort of form and sense in a world of chaos and disasters.

She sang to him for hours, Yiddish songs, Russian songs and the prayers in Hebrew. In this, too, Yossel seemed to find some comfort, sometimes tapping his foot, sometimes rocking to and fro. Sometimes his troubled brown eyes would fill with tears. When this happened, Chava knew she had reminded him of the warmth and love of a mother whose memory now only vaguely lingered on.

While the summer lasted and the evenings were warm, Asher would take Yossel outside and teach him to catch a ball or show him the flowers and trees, saying aloud the name of each one. When the evenings became cooler, Asher taught him chess and draughts. The child was exceptionally bright, soon showing great talent at the board games, and displaying an insatiable, though silent interest in all that others were happy to teach him.

At night, Asher and Chava would spend hours discussing his progress. "So, how were things today ?" Asher would begin, as soon as they were sure that he was sound asleep.

"Today was a little better, I think," Chava would reply. "He let me hug him once. We popped in to see Devorah and he accepted a biscuit from her. He looked at some children playing in the park. He wouldn't join them, of course. He stayed by my side. But he seemed interested at least."

One evening, when they were both beginning to despair of his ever communicating verbally again, Chava said to Asher, "Do you know what I think, Asherel? I think aside from everything else, he's angry. He's so full of anger, he's almost ready to burst. I feel that if we could find a way to channel this anger, he'd be able to cope more easily with the world. We've got to find a way to help him express himself."

The next day, Chava went out and bought crayons and blank paper, a little cross with herself that she had taken so long to think of this way of stimulating Yossi. When she came home, she drew pictures of birds and houses and trees while he watched. Finally, she placed a crayon in his hand and showed him how he could create his own shapes and colours on the paper.

"You can draw a picture if you like, Yossel, " she finished. "I'm going to make us some lunch and you can sit here and see if you enjoy using the crayons."

The first day, Chava saw Yossel simply made small lines, learning to use crayons and seeing the effect of the different colours. After a few days, he only used two colours, black and red. His pictures were unclear in their meaning, but definite in their mood of violence and sadness. Yossel worked at his drawings with extreme concentration. At times Chava would notice he was not even aware of her presence in the room, that his face was red and his breathing heavy.

It was over this period that he began to wake up at night screaming and sobbing. Because he would not speak, they could only guess at his nightmares. As long as they were needed, they stayed at his side, holding his hand, stroking his hair, assuring him over and over again they would always protect him, that nothing that he had experienced would ever happen again. After all, they were young themselves and optimistic about life in general.

The daytime pictures became more savage and the nightmares seemed to worsen. Chava felt as if she couldn't stand to watch much more of his suffering. When she suggested to Asher that they hide the crayons away from Yossel, he disagreed.

"Let it all come out," he said. "It's like a festering sore inside his body. This is the only way he has to purge himself of his memories and his feelings. If we can just be strong enough to get through this period, I'm sure there'll be a light at the end of the tunnel."

Chava was not so sure. The tense days and sleepless nights were beginning to affect her. She was no longer confident about the possibility that Yossel could ever behave like a normal child. She was tired and overwrought.

One freezing January day, six months after Yossel's arrival, Chava took the child to an afternoon orchestral concert of light music at the Opera and Ballet House. For the first time in months, Chava revelled in her own enjoyment and tried to forget about the pain of the disturbed little boy seated next to her. She marvelled at the old imposing edifice, gazing with wonder at the beauty of the crystal chandeliers and the magnificent artwork visible from both the gallery and boxes.

She sat with rapt attention throughout the performance, letting the music flow over her and heal her troubled soul. She only broke her concentration to remind herself to tell Asher one of the greatest advantages of communism in Russia was that even the poorest people could enjoy theatre, music and ballet. The tickets were only one rouble for herself and a half rouble for Yossel.

As they made their way home through Lenin Street after the performance, Chava felt calm and happy. The trivial thought entered her mind that they should have kept the name Richelieuvskaya instead of Lenin for the old street leading out of the grandiose theatre house. It was somehow more fitting.

Holding Yossel by the hand, she headed for the closest park, wishing to hold on to the peaceful respite she had gained. At the park, she seated herself on a bench, lifting up the collar of her coat to keep out the cold winter air and doing the same for Yossel. Yossel, she noticed, was staring at her intently, to the extent that it made her feel uncomfortable. She tried to keep calm by saying to herself, "Everything is in Hashem's hands. What will be, will be. It doesn't help to worry. Asher and I have done our very best to heal this darling boy.   The rest is up to the Ribbono Shel Olam."

But Yossel was now tugging at her hands, forcing her to concentrate on him. "What is it, my boy?" she smiled at him. "Do you need to go to the bathroom? I am sure we will find one here," she said, as she looked around her and began to rise from her bench.

But Yossel pushed her back onto the bench. He kept his eyes fixed on her, swallowing hard, opening and closing his mouth. With a flash of insight, Chava realised he was trying to speak. She sat bolt upright, smiling warmly and expectantly, "Yes, Yossel, tell me," she coaxed.

With great difficulty, in a voice that cracked from lack   of   use,   Yossel   forced   out   two   words, "Music...beautiful."

A second later Chava found Yossel in her arms. She was laughing and crying at the same time. "Yes, my boy, it was beautiful music, beautiful......," she said over and over again rocking him, "beautiful...... music. But what I heard just now was the most beautiful music ever!"

A small crowd of women and children had gathered around them.   "Are you all right?"   a matronly woman asked her.

"Oh, I'm fine, thank you," she answered, a little embarrassed at the spectacle they were making of themselves. "I'm just perfect, absolutely wonderful."

They took the trolley car home. Chava kept Yossel on her lap. She smiled with joy all the time, holding on to the words which had been spoken and the closeness reached between them. Yossel was smiling - a tiny half-smile - his first that Chava could remember. It showed a sense of pride and self-satisfaction. Chava's heart soared with delight even more.

At home, she took out some building blocks for him to play with while she prepared supper, dying with excitement to tell Asher the news, knowing she could not reach him as he was on his way home.

Yossel went to fetch his crayons and paper. Chava could only hope and pray that the mood of hopefulness which had been created, would not be destroyed.

When Asher did finally come home, Chava was busy setting the table and Yossel was drawing on the floor. Asher didn't notice Chava's expectant, smiling face and strode through the living room, on his way to the bedroom, saying, "Hello, Chava. Hello Yossel."

The "Hello, Asher," he heard in reply was barely audible. Chava saw him stop dead in his tracks and turn to face Yossel who again sat with a half-smile, a smug look on his face. Asher, a look of disbelief in his eyes, looked questioningly at Chava who nodded excitedly.

The mood in their apartment that evening was festive. Although Yossel did not speak much more that evening, he looked proud and happy. It held promise for the future.

Later that evening, when Yossel had gone to sleep, Chava made two telephone calls to spread the good news. The one was to Devorah and Chaim whose first child was due to arrive shortly. The second was to Freida who had brought Yossel to them. She had visited their home once a week without fail, checking on Yossel, whom one could see she still loved, fulfilling more than her promise to Yossel's mother. Chava hated these intrusions, hated to feel that once a week her home and her mothering abilities were being inspected, but she understood what motivated the sad woman, and she let it be.

When Chava told her about Yossel, Freida let out a shriek of delight, saying, "I had a feeling you two could do it. I knew all along you would succeed!" Chava was grateful for the woman's praise, knowing that Yossel, whom she had brought out of the camps with her, was as precious to her as her own children had been. After Yossel began to speak, Freida no longer visited. She would telephone and speak to him asking him whether he felt well, was eating enough, was keeping warm, satisfied just to hear his voice and to be assured of his welfare.

That night, as Chava went to switch off the light, she glanced at the picture Yossel had drawn early that evening. A new colour adorned the paper. In the middle of the harsh red and black, there was a bright yellow, round ball of fire. On a cold, wintry day in Odessa, Yossel had finally found the sun!

CHAPTER EIGHT

For a little while, it seemed that the calm and joy enveloping Chava and Asher was going to last. Devorah gave birth to a baby boy who was named Moshe after Devorah's young brother who had died during the Holocaust. His Brit Milah, performed by his grandfather, Dov, was an auspicious occasion, seeming to be part of the unbelievable revival of Jewish life from the ashes of the Holocaust. Because it was accomplished with apparent ease and no-one felt too fearful, it also seemed to signify an apparent improvement in the attitude of the authorities towards religious practice.

During the festivities after the Bris, Chava assisted Devorah with the baby, but Asher met and spoke to two other couples, Sasha and Rosa Dubnowitz, and Eli and Marina Rochinsky, who were discussing the possibility of opening a Yiddish school in Odessa. They had children of school-going age and wanted to give them a knowledge of Jewish traditions and culture. They agreed to meet at Asher and Chava's apartment the following evening to discuss the issue in detail.

Chava felt excited the entire day waiting for the meeting. They were going to be with other young Jewish couples who were interested in maintaining some level of Jewish education and practice in Odessa. The Yiddish school, Chava felt, could provide a measure of protection for Yossel, who would take some time in learning to communicate with members of the outside world. Although she was tired, having prepared most of the refreshments for the Bris, she baked again, anxious to please her guests.

That evening, after they had all seated themselves and exchanged the usual pleasantries, Eli, a big man with bright, piercing eyes and a full beard, who seemed used to taking command, began by saying, "We must tread very carefully, my friends. We don't know how the authorities are going to react to our request."

"But don't you think things have eased up a little for us since the war, since everybody saw where antisemitism could end if it wasn't stopped?" Chava asked.

"No, I don't think so, my dear," Eli replied. "Let's examine the evidence without hiding from the truth. We know, for example, that the Nazi murder squads rarely had more than nine hundred German soldiers at their disposal, but they were able to kill tens of thousands of Jews at one time because of the zealous participation of Russians, and in particular, our Ukrainian neighbours. Just think of Babi Yar for example. Now, straight after the war, when we Jews would like to see some retributive justice, Stalin makes a law forbidding Jews to take revenge on Russian and Ukrainian Nazi collaborators. Anyone trying to kill these murderers will be shot."

"We're aware, too, that all efforts to gather and publish information on the suffering of our people, the deaths of four million Jews who lived in the U.S.S.R., is being stifled. To add insult to this terrible injury, while all other nationalities are mentioned specifically, no special mention has been made of the part played by our Jewish war heroes, both as soldiers and as partisans."

"Sasha here is a general, involved for four years in the war. He was among the first to liberate Leningrad. I headed a partisan group and risked my life over and over again to help the Motherland. Have you any idea how we feel when the authorities carefully avoid mention of our contribution to the war effort?"

Sasha was a thin, wiry man with wavy brown hair. He seemed to weigh each word he spoke, not wanting to waste time. One could actually see him thinking each thought through carefully. He cleared his throat, signalling to the others that he wished to speak.

"The last war took a huge death toll on the Russian people - they are talking about twenty-five million. During this immense war effort, the government couldn't help but relax its political stranglehold on the people. For people of other nationalities, in particular Ukrainians, for example, who were never happy to give up their independence, there's been a strong militant aspect to their nationalistic ideals. Stalin will never tolerate this. It will be stopped at all costs. The question is whether Stalin will be able to accept our form of nationalism - our desire to teach our children Yiddish and Hebrew, and our traditions and culture."

"Well, it looks as if they're still letting the Jewish Anti-Fascist Committee function. They let it run throughout the war, and thanks to them we again have the pleasure of one Yiddish publication, 'Eynikayt'." Asher mentioned. "The committee are doing everything in their power to rekindle Yiddish culture, encouraging and promoting Yiddish authors, poets, dramatists and artists."

Rosa, a slender woman wearing long pants and a warm pullover pushed back her unruly mop of auburn hair and suggested excitedly, "Well, perhaps these people can help us to establish the school? They probably know how to approach the authorities about the matter."

"I could contact Shlomo Mikhoels in Moscow," said Sasha." He's the head of the committee and I know him personally."

"That's an excellent idea!" exclaimed Eli excitedly.

"I'll speak to him this week and report back to you at our next meeting," said Sasha, making a note in his diary.

Marina came to help Chava bring in the tea. She was a beautiful woman with jet-black hair and sad, brown eyes. "You were very quiet, this evening," Chava said to her, smiling.

"Yes," she answered, "I was. I have to admit I'm not altogether certain we should be trying to set up a Yiddish school. Eli has his heart set on the idea. He also insisted that we circumcize our boys when they were born, even though it was so dangerous. Personally, I have no feelings about religion, because I know nothing about it. I look at you and your husband and Eli and I see a flame burning in your eyes, but I have no idea what ignites the flame."

"Then we shall have to teach you, won't we?" said Chava, putting her arm around Marina.

Over tea, there was a lot of pleasant chatter. Eli and Marina spoke about their two boys aged four and two, who were both conceived and born among partisan groups in the forests. Sasha and Rosa spoke with great pride about their daughter, Irina, who was already six years old. They related tales of their life in Moscow and also described their delight at having been given permission to move to Odessa just a year before.

For the first time, Chava felt confident enough to speak about Yossel and the hurdles they had to overcome to reach him. Her words, she felt, were heard with sympathy and understanding.

Towards the end of the evening, Sasha turned the conversation back to the school. "What if we should be refused?" he asked everyone. "You know, a lot of Jews are talking about Birobidjan. They're saying perhaps it'll be a haven for us. It's far from Moscow. The authorities promise the Jews total control and autonomy. We could learn agriculture. There, they must grant us our own schools."

"Don't trust Stalin," Eli whispered as they all got up to go. "Don't have faith in any promises. If there's one thing we've learned over the centuries it's that we have been let down and persecuted time and time again. We must only trust in ourselves."

As Asher and Chava cleared the tea cups, Yossel, looking sleepy and tousled, strolled into the room. "Were we making too much noise? Did we wake you with all our chatter?" Chava asked him.

"Not really. I'm not used to Asher's bed. I like it here on the sofa best."

"Then let's settle you here, my darling, "Chava said. As Chava was putting on his blankets, Yossel asked, "Asher, what's Birobidjan?"

Asher sat down. "Birobidjan is an area miles and miles away from here, miles from anywhere, near the Manchurian border. In the late nineteen twenties - that's a long time ago - the Russian government declared this province a special area for Jews."

"Then why don't we go there? " Yossel demanded to know. "We could be safe there."

Asher looked at the little boy, sad that he should be so young in years and yet so old in his understanding of the vagaries of life. He answered him as honestly as he could. "Because we've heard the climate there is harsh and the soil swampy and mosquito-infested. Because we've heard that Birobidjan has failed as a national home. The Jewish population there has never reached more than about fourteen thousand people. Aside from anything else, we don't have any special feeling for the area, like we have, for example, for Yerushalyim where the Temple was and for Tzfat and Tiberias where great rabbis lived."

"What's the name of the area of *Yerushalayim* and Tzfat and Tiberias?" Yossel asked.

"Other people call it Palestine, but Jewish people call it Eretz Yisrael, the Land of Israel," Asher replied.

"Who does it belong to, now?" Yossel persisted.

"A while ago, it belonged to the Turks. Right now, it belongs to the British. But do you know, that because of all that has happened to us over the last few years, people are talking about giving some of that land to the Jews?"

"Really?" Yossel exclaimed excitedly. "Really, Asher?"

"Yes, really and truly," replied Asher with a smile.

"Could we go there, Asher, could we?"

Again Asher smiled, this time, sadly. "Better not to wish for the stars," he said softly.

He ruffled Yossel's hair, "and now, my boy, stop worrying and get some sleep."

CHAPTER NINE

More meetings were held over the next few weeks. The three couples wanted to be sure they could present a credible proposal to the Ministry of Education, indicating the numbers of Jewish children who would make use of a Yiddish school, the teachers available and the assurances to the authorities that no anti-Soviet propaganda would be espoused at the school.

The truth was they were thoroughly enjoying their meetings. After they had finished discussing the school, they would talk about the latest play that was on at the newly established Yiddish Theatre in Odessa. Sometimes they'd go on to reading Yiddish poetry recently published and sometimes they would chat about the possibility of finding a Hebrew teacher so they could learn Hebrew together.

There was an unmentioned feeling of excitement and joy that filled these meetings - a sense of belonging and of purpose. Chava looked forward to the day of their meeting with the authorities with hope and expectation. She was totally upset, however, the day before when the men suddenly decided they would go on their own.

"It's safer this way," Asher explained to her. "We don't know how the authorities are going to react. There are rumours in the air. If anything happens to us, at least the wives will be left to take care of the children."

Hearing this, Chava burst into tears. "If there's any chance, any chance whatsoever that something terrible can happen to you, Asherel, then I don't want you to go. Do you hear me? You're not to go!"

"It would have been my sister Leah's wish, and it's my wish, to give Yossel a Jewish education. I have to do everything in my power to achieve this. If I fail, I fail, but I have to try," he replied firmly.

The next day, Asher came home from the meeting with the officials at the Ministry looking nervous and despondent. He told Chava how they had carefully worded their request to include a reminder that Yiddish schools had been re-established in various other soviet cities since the war, including Kovno and Vilna in Lithuania.

He described how the officials had shouted, "It's not necessary! Most of your children speak Russian now. Why do you want to fill their heads with old-fashioned ideas about religion? Do you want to spread thoughts of Zionist imperialism and bourgeois ideals?"

Eli had bravely taken a different line, reminding the clerks that all other nationalities, for example Germans, Poles, Lithuanians and Greeks were permitted to establish schools which taught in the mother tongue.

Again the shouting had begun. "Jews are a different case altogether! All Yiddish schools will shortly be closed down. The Kremlin have decided these schools are against the interests of the Motherland!"

What Asher never told Chava was that the names of the three men and all their details had been taken down, with a special mocking glance at the word *Yivrei*, Jew, that was stamped on their internal passports. In the Utopia the communists had supposedly created, it seemed the issue of no discrimination on the basis of race, religion and nationality was forgotten when it came to the question of Jews.

It was over this period that Chava began to understand what Asher had gone through in his early years. Whereas she had never been afraid to be Jewish in Kovno before the war and in Samarkand during the war, now she felt a constant gnawing fear which plagued her days and nights.

A woman in her forties, known to be an informer, approached Marina and asked to be included in 'the little Jewish study group'. The group realized they were being watched and no further meetings were held. Asher warned Chava and Yossel to be careful what they said at the Synagogue. The *shammes* and the *gabbai* were thought to be informers.

When Chava later looked back on those years, she could make no sense of the time and the occurrences. A black period began in her life which intensified as Stalin's madness worsened and his henchmen rallied around to fulfill his commands, fearing for their own lives. It seemed as though every second person was an informer. They trusted no-one but the Gutsteins and the two couples who had recently become their friends. All serious discussions took place outside the home, in parks and on pavements.

Despite the joy Chava had in bringing up Yossel, he was more like a younger brother to her than a child, and she and Asher had to deal with the pain of their own childlessness while Devorah and Chaim's family grew to three children.

Like a distant shore being pounded again and again by storms, she received news that was primarily spread among the Jewish community by word of mouth rather than through the newspapers. She would later remember certain incidents. One day Asher came home looking pale and haggard. "What happened?" she asked him.

"Later," he said, looking pointedly at Yossel. They always tried to protect Yossel, mostly to prevent him from becoming too angry at what he could not help.

When Yossel was asleep, Asher told her, "Over the past few days, hundreds of Jewish intellectuals have been arrested - writers, poets, actors, artists and musicians!"

She was aghast. "What for?" she asked.

"Some for bourgeois nationalism and others for Zionism," he replied.

"Do you think any will be executed?" she whispered, terrified.

"Yes," he replied, "those who are lucky will be forbidden to continue with their work, and so will have financial worries. Those who aren't so lucky, will be imprisoned or sent to Siberia. But quite a lot will be executed.

"What's bourgeois nationalism?" she wanted to know.

"I'm not sure, but for the Jews, to write a Yiddish poem or play, to draw a painting with a Jewish theme, to try to document what the Jews of the Soviet Union experienced during the Holocaust - those are crimes of bourgeois nationalism. Any Jew who expresses a love for the land of Israel is also committing a crime of either bourgeois nationalism or Zionism."

"But the Russians themselves are promoting the creation of a state for the Jewish people in the international arena," she whispered.

"Yes," agreed Asher, also lowering his voice, "it would seem that those in power feel that right now, that is the best political stance to take in the outside world. But if Jews here express a love for another land, then life here cannot be totally perfect, and that idea is a terrible threat to the authorities."

One day, in November 1947, Asher phoned her excitedly from work. He almost never asked to use the phone at work unless it was an emergency, so she panicked on hearing his voice. "Is everything all right?" she asked him quickly.

"Yes, everything is wonderful," he shouted. "Levitan, the radio announcer, has just told us the United Nations has voted in favour of creating a state for the Jewish people in Palestine."

"Oh, Asherel, that's wonderful," she shouted back, "just wonderful."

"Let's have a little party tonight," she said gaily. "I don't think Devorah and Chaim will be able to leave the children, Baby Rochel is still so tiny. But I'm sure the Rochinskys and Dubnowitzes will come!"

The building where Chava and Asher stayed was adjacent to another apartment block. The distance between the two buildings was so small that it was possible to see into a neighbour's living room on the same floor.

As Chava spoke, she noticed a curtain being drawn back, but she wasn't sure.

The small party that evening was so joyous, Chava felt she would burst. All the children were present to celebrate the occasion. Chava looked across at Yossel laughing together with the Rochinsky boys, while Irinia looked on. She felt so grateful for reaching this point in their lives, despite the pain they had endured.

Asher had been promoted at work and was receiving a good salary. Yossel had miraculously fitted in well at his new school. The principal, secretly Jewish herself, allowed Yossel to be excused from writing on Shabbos although she insisted on his presence in the classroom. On the whole, they couldn't complain. And now, after two thousand years, there was going to be a homeland for the Jewish people as the prophets had promised and the prayers had entreated.

For the second time that day, she noticed the flick of a curtain.

A knot of fear pierced her stomach. She whispered to Asher, who in turn whispered to the others. Eli had been teaching everyone a Hebrew song he had learned before the war. He quickly changed to a Russian song, and everybody sang as loudly as possible, just in case others were listening.

Chava couldn't sleep that night. She wasn't sure why. Was it over-excitement, or was it fear, a feeling of dread of something unknown, something to come?

By the morning, after a restless night, she knew that it was dread, and when members of the Secret Police blocked the entrance to their apartment as Asher wanted to leave for work, she was hardly surprised.

One part of her brain registered relief that Yossel had left early for school and so had not had to witness Asher's arrest. Another part registered the harsh, clipped words of the policemen. With a clarity of thought and purpose, she packed Asher's warmest clothes, and a parcel of food, consisting mainly of dried and canned goods.

Asher's hands trembled as he helped her, but hers, though icy, were surprisingly steady. They did not speak as they feverishly worked together in the room where they had shared their thoughts, their feelings and their love. There was nothing left to say.

Silently, Chava took off her watch and a silver bracelet he had bought her for their previous anniversary. They were not expensive items, but who knew what would tickle a guard's fancy if he was open to bribery? She began to take off her ring, but Asher took her hands, stopping her, his eyes filling with tears. The ring was a symbol of their marriage, of their being bound together. She should only take it off if she heard he would never return.

The strident, clipped words of the policemen again intruded. The jewellery was hastily thrust into a pocket. Asher and Chava looked deeply into each other's eyes, and then turned towards the policemen. Chava saw a cold impassive look on their faces. Seconds later, Asher was gone.

Chava walked slowly towards the window and opened it wide. The curtain of the adjacent apartment flapped in the summer breeze. There was no sign of movement but Chava felt certain she was being watched.

"Take a good look, my enemy, at whom you have so needlessly harmed!" she mouthed clearly.

Then she ran to the bedroom, threw herself down on the bed, and sobbed.

After some time, when she could cry no more, the terrible task of telling Yossel about Asher's arrest was uppermost in her mind. She wondered how Yossel would react. Would he again retreat to his own world of silence and aloofness where nothing could touch him?

When he came home, she sat him down and gave him his lunch. After he had finished and began to look questioningly at her because of her helpless silence, she sat down and began to speak. "You remember, Yossel, how Asher and I promised you we would always protect you, that nothing you had experienced in the war would ever happen again. Well, we were wrong. We don't really have control over our lives, especially not here, where we live."

She swallowed and tried hard to continue. "They...the Secret Police came for Asher today."

Sobbing, she could not continue. Then she found Yossel in her arms, a little six-year-old who had suffered the unspeakable, trying to comfort her.

"Please be strong for me, my Yossel, please. I need you to be well. I can't be strong for both of us!"

Through her tears, Chava felt Yossel put his arm around her. The relief she felt at his reaction to the frightening news and the comfort she took from him made her almost want to smile.

"At least this small mercy," she said to herself. "At least this!"

CHAPTER TEN

By the end of that day, during fraught, coded conversations with Rosa and Marina, Chava learned that Eli and Sasha had also been arrested. It appeared they would all be charged with Zionism. By the end of the following day, Chava had had a quick visit from a sad, shocked Sasha. The trials had taken place in the morning, he explained. He had been released with a severe warning because of his position as a general during the war years. Asher and Eli had both been sentenced to fifteen years of exile in Siberia.

Over the next few days, the same steely strength which had seen Chava through the bombing of Odessa and her departure from the city, returned. There was not much point in crying, she realized, when she had to be strong for Yossel and make a living for the two of them. Even if she was not hungry and saw no point in carrying on, Yossel's sad, angry face would come before her, forcing her to keep going, to search for work, and get through one day at a time.

The manager of the textile factory who had admired Asher's creativity and diligence and sorely missed his input, took pity on Chava and gave her work as a typist. She earned barely enough for herself and Yossel to live on. Her days were long, hard and lonely. In the evenings, she would try to be cheerful for Yossel's sake. She was aware that aside from everything else, the youngster was learning to let himself into the apartment and care for himself during the long hours it took for her to get home each afternoon.

Devorah and Chaim helped and comforted her as much as they could. But they were struggling themselves and terrified of the authorities. A fourth baby was on the way. Chaim was never lucky enough to find a job that did not involve working on Shabbos, and so he did odd jobs, which only just kept them all fed.

Their devotion to Judaism (and, Chava suspected, their secret teaching of Torah to other Jews) were considered criminal to the authorities, and so they tried to live inconspicuous lives, their poverty and deprivation almost being a protection against police interference.

Uncle Dov stayed with Devorah and Chaim for part of the year, but spent most of his time with Aharon in Kiev where they shared an apartment. They eked out a living by fixing watches. Chava suspected that they, too, taught Torah in secret, living a twilight existence to avoid being noticed by the authorities.

During those years, Chava and Yossel found they derived the most comfort from Marina and her sons, Yuri and Boris, who were experiencing the same pain and anguish. Yuri was in Yossel's class at school, so they knew each other well, and for the most part the two six-year olds were sweet to little Boris, two years younger, letting him participate in their games.

On Friday evenings, Marina would come for Shabbos dinner, always bringing with her a contribution to the meal - some apples or a melon for dessert, some herring and tomatoes for the main course and occasionally some sweets for the children.

With bittersweet tears glistening in her eyes, Chava would watch Yossel reciting the Kiddush, traditionally the job of the master of the house. As time progressed, Yossel taught his young friends the prayer and they would also take a turn to have this honour. Marina and her boys eventually learned all the customary songs and prayers for Friday evening from Shalom Aleichem to the end of the *benching*.

They would participate in all the proceedings, delighted when Chava and Yossel would talk about the portion of the week or other Torah matters. Chava was amazed at how much Yossel had picked up from Asher's words, remembering ideas Asher had spoken about years before, when Chava had presumed that Yossel was lost in his own world and not absorbing much.

During the summer months, Marina and Chava would often go down to the sea on a Sunday, taking a ferry boat from the port area to Laungeron Beach, where the boys would swim and they would all enjoy a picnic. The two women could have taken their children and spent a few weeks at the Bolshoi Phantam, in the holiday cottages provided for rich and poor alike, but both needed to keep working to support themselves and both wished to stay close to home, where letters or news might arrive. Every human being hopes for good things to happen - for miracles.

The two small families were a buffet for each other against the harshness and loneliness of their worlds and against the storm rising around them. For after 1948, the new crime one could commit was called "rootless cosmopolitanism", which apparently meant that one did not show enough interest in Soviet ideals and in the Motherland.

This new campaign of Stalin was directly antisemitic. Shlomo Mikhoels, chairman of the Jewish

Anti-fascist Committee, and director of the Yiddish theatre in Moscow was secretly murdered by the KGB. The Anti-Fascist Committee was dissolved. The publication of 'Eynikayt' was prohibited. All Yiddish schools set up after the war were liquidated, and Jewish writers and intellectuals were arrested and deported.

In the midst of all this came a ray of sunshine through Marina who had heard along the Jewish grapevine that Golda Meir had visited Moscow. It was on Yom Kippur, at a small secret *minyan* arranged by Chaim and Uncle Dov, when Marina whispered the news to Chava.

Later that day, during a break in the *davening*, Chava took Yossel to their favourite park, and while shivering in the chilly autumn air, she asked him, "Yossel, do you remember, just before Asher was arrested, we were so happy because the world said the Jewish people could have their own land in Palestine?"

Yossel nodded vigorously.

"Well, in May of this year, our wish came and the State of Israel was created. There was a terrible war afterwards with the Arabs, but in the end the Jews won. Israel has its own Parliament, called the Knesset. One of the ladies of the Knesset is called Golda Meir, who comes from Kiev.

"Anyway, over the last couple of weeks, she's been visiting the Soviet Union. On Rosh Hashanah she went to the Great Shul of Moscow, hoping to meet the few old Jews who usually come to Shul on Yomtov. But do you know what? Fifty thousand Jews were there to meet her, touch her and ask 'Is it true? Is there really a new State of Israel?' It was the Moscow celebration of the new Jewish State."

The way Yossel's sad little face lit up lifted Chava's spirits. "Are there many Jews in Moscow?" Yossel wanted to know.

"Yes," Chava answered, "there are plenty of Jews in Moscow. The amazing thing is that so many people came to see a lady from the land of Israel."

She marvelled to herself, "It's been thirty years since the Communist revolution. Nobody keeps Shabbos, nobody keeps *kosher*. There are no marriages under the *chupa* and no Bris Milot, and yet the Jewish people have not forgotten who they are. What a remarkable phenomenon!"

"Perhaps.... perhaps when Asher comes back, we could apply for permission to go there," Yossel ventured optimistically.

"Oh, Yossel!" was all Chava could bring herself to say. How could she tell him that many of the men who were exiled to Siberia never returned? They died of cold, hunger and excessive labour. She felt a familiar lump in her throat and wrapped her arms about herself to stave off the loneliness she felt at yet another festival without her husband.

Then, for Yossel's sake she forced herself to smile and added, "Well, perhaps. But we won't talk about this to other people, will we? It's too dangerous. We don't know which of your friends are informers and we don't need any more trouble."

With an understanding far beyond his years through life experience, Yossel nodded, and Chava knew without a doubt she could trust him.

They cheered up a little over Succot. The Gutsteins invited them to eat in their Succah. This helped them over their sadness at Asher not being there to make one for them. A special mercy and joy was a letter that arrived from Asher. Much of the letter had been blotted out by the censors. It was also clear that only a few of the many food parcels and letters they had sent, had reached Asher. Yet seeing Asher's handwriting gave Chava hope and helped her to face a bleak future.

Chava kept Asher's letter next to her bed and reread it every night before going to sleep. It was a great comfort:

My dearest Chava and Yossel,

The High Holy Days are approaching - another festival without you. I hope you have received my previous letters. I have received three letters from you and two food parcels, for which I offer my grateful thanks. Thank you, Yossel, for your beautiful pictures. I am only sorry they are all in black and grey. Perhaps next time you will include some blues, yellows and greens.

Everything here is as expected. (Here a whole paragraph was erased by the authorities.) *I have seen Eli and he is all right.*

I wish you both a gute yohr. *May we all be blessed with faith, strength, good health and tranquillity this year and always. You are both constantly in my prayers. Thoughts of you both keep me alive. Chava, I kiss the light of your eyes.*

Yours forever,
Asher.

At first, Chava would cry each time she read the letter. Later, she became less prone to crying. A harsh bitterness replaced the tears, sustaining her through a lonely, frightening existence.

Daily, the newspapers published articles laced with lies and accusations against Jews. They ranted against those who had dared to adopt Russian names and alerted the public to the danger of Jewish spies and traitors. The arrests continued on a massive scale. Sheer terror gripped the population.

By late 1952, it was reported in the newspapers Stalin had 'discovered' that his inner circle of doctors, most of them Jewish, who had guarded his health for twenty years, were planning to murder him. Everyone knew the accusations were false, yet they also knew with certainty all the accused would be found guilty and executed. As 1953 was ushered in, rumours went around the Jewish community that Stalin was planning to deport all the Jews to Siberia.

With the experiences of the Second World War fresh in their minds, the Jews trembled in terror. People were afraid to go far from home lest there would be a sudden deportation order and the family would be split up.

Over and over again, Chava told Yossel about various places in the apartment where he could hide, telling him that if anything should happen, he should try his best to hide and wait for her.... wait for her...

It was almost Purim and Uncle Dov insisted they make a proper little Purim party for the children, *hamentassen* and all. Marina and her boys were also invited. Encouraged by Uncle Dov, who kept repeating, "It's Purim, it's a *mitzvah* to be happy," they all tried to put on a brave front for the children. As it had been so long since they had any light-hearted times, the children were delighted. They even sang and danced.

The next day, it seemed another Purim miracle had taken place. The radio announced Stalin was ill. From this, everyone understood that he was already dead, as they never announced when a high Party member became ill.

A few days before Pesach that year, Chava travelled as usual on the trolley car that took her home. En route, she realized she would soon be only twenty-six years old yet felt as though she were fifty. Yossel was now eleven and a half, but he too had known great tragedy and was old beyond his years.

When she opened her apartment door, she was shocked to find an old man, emaciated and unkempt sitting in her living room. She took fright, seeing no sign of Yossel, and for a few moments was speechless.

The old man looked up at her and asked "Do I look so different to you, Chavale?"

In a flash, Chava realized Asher had been released 'from the distant Siberian labour camp! He was alive, home, and she would make him well and strong again! A few seconds later they were all hugging each other and celebrating.

In 1954, when Asher and Chava had been married for nine years, and Yossel was almost Barmitzvah, they were blessed with their own special miracle. Chava was astonished to find she was pregnant. Later that year, she gave birth to a precious little girl. Born as she was after years of waiting, years of torment and suffering, she was called Natalya, for the sake of Russian anonymity, and Nechama after Chava's mother. Truly, that's what she was for all of them, their consolation.

CHAPTER ELEVEN

Chava would remember 1954 and 1955 as years of readjustment for them all. Asher had come back from Siberia a weakened man, in some aspects changed, with a bitterness that sometimes frightened her and a bronchial cough that was to remain with him always. During her pregnancy, she had thought more about restoring his health than her own condition. He never spoke much about his life in the camps, except occasionally to Yossel, when she was out of earshot.

After his return from Siberia, although their love for each other was strong and unwavering, they came to each other with new pasts. Asher was now an old *zek,* a labour camp inmate, Chava a survivor of a different kind, having learned something new about her own strength and abilities.

Yossel, the teenager, was tall for his age. As a result of his experiences as a toddler and during the recent years of Asher's absence, Yossel was no dreamy-eyed gawky adolescent. He had become a world-wise, thoughtful young man whose apparent strength and fearlessness often made Chava shiver with fear for him.

Once he came home and reported an incident of fighting with boys who had jeered at him for keeping a cap on his head all day. Chava suggested she and Asher speak to the boys' parents or the principal, but Yossel just laughed and said, "Eh, I can fight my own battles thank you!"

"You may get hurt one of these days, Yossel," Asher ventured.

His reply left them reeling. "You know, after all I've been through, I'm not afraid of anything any more, not even torture or death. This gives me a great feeling of freedom and strength."

Chava knew that wonderful as it was for him to have Asher home, Yossel had seen himself as her protector during Asher's absence, her 'man about the house', and it had been hard for him to relinquish that role even though he obviously felt relief and joy.

Natalya's entrance to the world at first threw them all into turmoil. Chava was new to mothering a tiny baby. Aside from the few brief hours looking after little Basha years before, she had never taken on such responsibilities. It sometimes made her feel tired and a little inept, despite all the joy. The loving advice of Devorah, Marina and Rosa helped her through, however, and once the first three months were over and Natalya began to sleep through the night, she felt stronger and more confident as a mother.

For Asher, Natalya became a symbol of miracles, of G-d's ultimate mercy after endless suffering. He was so in awe of the tiny, vulnerable creature who was his daughter that for months he was afraid to hold her, this precious evidence of hope and life. And Yossel had to come to terms with his unconscious jealousy of the new child in Asher and Chava's life.

When the first few traumatic months were over, when Chava became confident of her mothering abilities, when Asher would hold Natalya in his arms and sing her a Yiddish lullaby, when Yossel fell in love with the baby and transferred his fierce feelings of protection from Chava onto Natalya, then they truly became a family, secure in their love for each other. So it was Natalya became an important factor in binding them all together.

The spring of 1955 brought further reason for excitement. During September, a letter arrived from Israel addressed to Yossel. They all looked at the envelope for some minutes, marvelling at the stamp, and the sticker which said in Hebrew 'By Airmail', this object which had come all the way from the Holy Land.

Eventually, Yossel carefully opened the letter with a knife, to preserve the envelope intact. Seeing that it was written in Yiddish and knowing that his reading in that language was slow and halting, he passed the letter to Asher to read for him.

Asher read out aloud slowly:

> *Kibbutz Ein Gev*
> *Doar Na Tiveria*
> *Israel*

My dear Yossel,

Through a certain Mrs. Freida Romanev, formerly Mrs. Freida Gershon, who registered you as a displaced person after the war, I have recently confirmed that you are my nephew, the son of my brother, Meir Rivkin, who apparently died during the war.

My wife and I came to live in Israel before the war. We live on a Kibbutz in the Galilee. From the windows of our little home we can see beautiful Lake Kinneret. We have four children who are already in their twenties and have begun to make lives of their own. I am enclosing photographs of all of us, including our grandchildren, with names on the reverse side, so you can become acquainted with the family.

I have written to you several times and received no reply. We have heard that our people in Russia may now finally make contact with relatives and friends abroad, so I do hope this letter will reach you and we will receive an answer.

I was the oldest child of our family of seven children, and your father, Meir, was the sixth, so there was a big age difference between us. Nevertheless, I have fond memories of him as a youngster and can share these with you if you like.

We, your family, wish you and our dear brother and sister-in-law a Shana Tova, a good year, and send warm regards.

> *Your uncle,*
> *Pinchas*

This letter had a profound effect on Yossel. Asher had tried his best to tell him everything he remembered about Leah, his sister and Yossel's mother. Yossel loved to hear about her and about his maternal grandparents. They gave him a sense of who he was. He treasured a photograph of his mother Asher had kept throughout the war. But Asher had barely had time to get to know his brother-in-law before the war and so had very little to tell him about the paternal side of his family. The fact that Yossel heard from his uncle on his Jewish birthday gave the letter an almost mystical quality.

The photographs of his new-found family were closely studied, by all three of them. Not only was there an intense interest to see whom Yossel resembled, they held an enormous fascination because they were pictures of Jews who looked proud and relaxed, sun-tanned and healthy.

Over the next decade and more, as the propaganda against Israel became increasingly negative, these photographs and others which followed were evidence of a sense of pride and contentment that was, in fact, attainable in Israel.

With Asher's help, Yossel answered his uncle's letter and there continued to be a warm correspondence between them whenever the Russian authorities allowed it.

Another cause for hope and excitement was the news that a *yeshivah* was to open the following year in Moscow. It would be called Yeshivat Kol Yaakov and would be headed by Rabbi Shlomo Schlieffer. Donations to help with the establishment of this *yeshiva* were requested - and, of course, applications from interested students would be most welcome.

What amazed Asher and Chava then was the generosity of the Jewish community of Odessa. Asher, Chaim and a few other religious Jews took it upon themselves to raise funds. The Odessa community were proud of their handsome contribution of thirty-three thousand roubles. The Kiev community, which was even larger than theirs, had not been able to contribute at all.

Chava, holding Natalya on her lap, helped Asher and Yossel write a letter requesting Yossel's admission to the Yeshivah. At the same time as her heart soared with pride at the knowledge that he had both the desire and the ability to go, it sank at the thought of their nephew-child leaving home.

"Of course, we will still have to request a permit from the Ministry of the Interior, allowing you reside in Moscow," Asher concluded. "The main thing, however, is that you progress with your learning so that you can cope there. How would you like it if I asked Uncle Chaim to give you some lessons?"

Yossel readily agreed. Although Asher had taught him whatever he knew over the years, the new plans meant this knowledge would no longer suffice. Yossel began learning the Talmud in earnest with Chaim and made excellent progress. When Uncle Dov visited from Kiev, he too would teach the boy.

Secret Zionist and Hebrew study groups were again cautiously formed in Odessa, in the hope that things were improving for the Jews. Stalin was dead, many of his actions as a leader denigrated by the Party. Who knew? Perhaps under Krushchev, life was going to be better.

CHAPTER TWELVE

As Nikita Kruschev came into power, life seemed to be easier for the Jews. Certainly there were fewer antisemitic articles in the newspapers, as well as a more tolerant attitude towards religious practice in general.

Nevertheless, although they tried to maintain control over their lives and to foresee the actions of the authorities, they were never able to understand Kruschev or the Kremlin. The whole period was fraught with contradictions.

Despite the apparent easing of religious persecution, the Jewish people were still not allowed to create a federation of religious communities and therefore had no framework through which Jewish groups could construct synagogues and make religious articles. With this, came a ban on all contact as a group or community with other Jewish cultural organizations or religious communities outside Russia, even with those in other East European countries.

The Yeshivat Kol Ya'acov was indeed established, but few students from outside Moscow were granted permits to live there. Yossel was bitterly disappointed when his request for permission to live in Moscow was turned down. Asher, Chava and Chaim all shared Yossel's feelings. They had all looked forward to his growth in religious learning.

Most of the students who were allowed to attend came from faraway places like Georgia and Uzbekistan, giving evidence of the amazing efforts made by Chabad Chassidim who taught Judaism to their people in secret over the years. Once the small quota allowed had been filled, all other applications were refused because the authorities opposed expansion.

Although anti-Zionist propaganda was not absent from the media, it seemed reduced, both in quantity and in virulence. In fact, until the Sinai Campaign, the government had discussions and trade agreements with Israel. The Odessa Jews occasionally saw evidence of this when Israeli ships would appear in the Odessa harbour loading and off-loading cargo.

When the summer of 1956 arrived, Natalya was already two years old. On hot July and August days, Chava accompanied by Yossel, would take Natalya down to the sea. Yossel would swim and Chava would dangle Natalya's feet in the water. It was on such a day that Yossel wandered off to see a new ship that had come into the harbour. He stayed away a long time and then arrived back breathless and red-faced.

When he reached her, he exclaimed "Chava, Chava! You'll never guess what I saw! A ship from Israel, and sailors, Chava, who speak Hebrew just like we speak Russian and Yiddish, as if it's their mother tongue!"

Chava, too, felt excited, but she maintained her calm even though she was smiling joyfully. They were both aware of the curious, almost hostile stares of onlookers. "Tell me," she asked, "how did the sailors look?"

"Oh, tall and strong and proud - without fear, as if the whole world belonged to them!"

Chava's smile broadened even further.

"One sailor asked where he could find a *minyan* for tonight to say Kaddish for his brother who was killed during the war in Israel in 1948. He spoke to me in Yiddish so it was all right, we could communicate. I told him about the Shul in Lessnaya Street, in Peressyp. It's the better one. I feel ashamed of the one we go to. It's so old and run-down."

That evening, Yossel was insistent he and Asher go to the Shul in Peressyp to pray, even though they had to travel some distance to reach their destination. Asher, Chava noticed, did not put up too much of an argument. He too seemed to be looking forward to meeting young Israeli men.

A few hours later when they arrived home, Asher's back seemed a little straighter and Yossel seemed a little taller. They told Chava every detail they could remember about the sailor who said his name was Gid'on and his friend, Dani, who had accompanied him.

"But Mr. Rabinovich went and spoiled everything, Chava," Yossel burst out at the end.

"Oh, why's that?" she asked, glancing at Asher who was looking down at his soup with a wry smile on his face.

"He just embarrassed us all so. After the service, he went up and asked them 'Does everybody in Israel speak Yiddish?' to which Gid'on replied 'Oh, no, sir. Everyone in Israel speaks Hebrew, modern Hebrew'.

"Mr. Rabinovich was flabbergasted, absolutely flabbergasted. And if that wasn't bad enough, he had another question. 'Do they close all the shops on Shabbos?' Of course, the reply was 'yes'. 'Impossible. I don't believe it!' said Mr Rabinovich. Then Asher put him in his place and said, 'But, you see it is possible, Mr. Rabinovich'."

Despite the fear of being discovered, the three couples began to meet again in secret, usually at the Dubnowitz' home, which now seemed to be their safest venue. They were all fully aware of the risks they took by re-establishing their little group, but they could not restrain themselves from this activity, as if doing so would be a deprivation of life itself.

All the youngsters now insisted on being present at these warm encounters. Irina the oldest, was there, with flaming red hair like her mother's and her own bubbly personality. Yossel and Yuri sat next to each other. They were both fifteen years old and shared a close friendship. Young Boris, who was going to Chaim for Barmitzvah lessons, would sit next to his father, proud to be included in the group. Of course, little Natalya was with them, simply because she could not be left behind. On her unsteady little legs, she toddled around the room and was picked up and cuddled by everyone there.

The last meeting of the year was an interesting one for everybody. Sasha had been asked to prepare a summary of recent events so they could somehow prepare for the future. In his thoughtful, unassuming way, he tried to encourage the group, reminding them of the opening of Moscow's Yeshiva, the Israeli sailors in the Odessa harbour, evidence of trade relations with Israel, and the apparent easing of the authorities with regard to religious practice.

"But," Sasha continued, "I cannot help reminding you also of the darker side of the picture. The KGB carries on waging its war on Zionism with undiminished vigour. It has paid special attention to Zionist nuclei that have begun to form in the cities and their contacts with the Israeli Embassy in Moscow."

With a slight shiver, Chava remembered hearing the news of the twenty-one Jews from Moscow, Leningrad and Malakhova who were arrested the previous year after prolonged observation. They were all tried secretly in Moscow and given prison sentences from two to ten years. Even more frightening and closer to home had been the further arrests and trials of Zionist group members in Odessa, Kiev and Latvia. In August, three members of the Israeli diplomatic mission, Kahat, Sela and Levanon had been expelled from the Soviet Union for contacting those on trial and actively encouraging them.

"The real blow," Sasha continued, "was the Sinai Campaign. It showed us clearly the Soviet Union's desire to strengthen its relationship with the Arab countries. All this led to a serious deterioration in Soviet-Israeli relations. I don't believe we will see Israeli ships in our harbour for some time."

At the end of the meeting, Rosa taught everyone a few new Hebrew words she had recently looked up, and they all sang some Yiddish tunes - very softly, so they would not be heard, and slowly, so the youngsters could pick up the words.

The optimistic note on which they tried to conclude the meeting did not seem to help any of them, however. Chava noticed when they left their backs were still a little bent, their faces were unsmiling and there was fear in their eyes. It was this look of fear which Jewish visitors to the Soviet Union found most disturbing when they visited the Soviet Union over the years.

CHAPTER THIRTEEN

In 1957, Chava had no choice but to look for work again. The food available after standing in queues for hours was meagre and tasteless as well as overpriced. One had to try to purchase extra rations from other not quite legal sources, so that the children, at least, could be provided with the basic proteins and vitamins they needed.

Asher would stand at the roadside leading into the city hoping to be able to buy fresh fruit and vegetables from one of the truck drivers bringing produce into town from the rural areas. It was a dangerous exercise and involved bribery. They all needed new coats and shoes, very expensive commodities in Russia. A good, new coat would take Asher's entire month's salary.

Asher, they knew, would never be promoted. His Jewishness and his record of imprisonment made that fact certain, although the manager of his factory often asked his advice and indicated that had things been different, he would not have hesitated to raise his position and salary.

So, when Natalya was close to three years old, Chava had no option but to place her in day care provided by the State. Chava had worked efficiently and conscientiously in her previous position as secretary, and the manager of Asher's factory was so keen to have her back, he created a secretarial position for her, for which Chava was extremely grateful.

Nevertheless, it broke her heart to leave Natalya with strangers. She was angry when, during the first few months, Natalya came down with every cough, cold and even chicken pox, brought into the creche by the other little ones. Whoever finished his 'working day' first, collected Natalya and brought her home. More often than not, it was Yossel who went to fetch her, make her a snack and play with her until her tired parents came home.

It became quite a joke with the boys at school. Yossel would have a 'painful knee' or 'pulled muscle' when it was time for after-school sports, and he would even turn down an excellent game of chess with a much-respected opponent, because he chose to fetch Natalya early.

Yossel's interest in art, as well as his talents in that sphere, had grown. After fetching Natalya, he would often take her with him to visit the older, more beautiful buildings of Odessa which had escaped demolition by Kruschev, telling her of the pleasure he took in their shape and form. It did not matter that Natalya was too young to understand. It gave him the opportunity to indulge in his developing interest.

While Yossel was tall, muscular and thin, Yuri was sturdier in build, taking after his broadshouldered father. In temperament, too, Yuri shared his father's qualities of leadership and forthrightness. Yossel, however, because he was who he was, a baby of the camps, a silent child, remained a quieter version of Yuri, yet a young man who burned inwardly.

In August, the two young friends made up their minds to travel to Moscow to see the Israeli delegates at the Youth Festival. Of course, it was Yuri who made the casual announcement at the July meeting held at Sasha and Rosa's home. Before any of the older people could say anything, Irina quickly asked if she could go, too. Her parents immediately answered, "Absolutely not!"

Asher, Chava and Marina then tried to argue with the boys, who seemed adamant in their decision. But it was Eli who took their side and eventually won all the others over.

"Let them go," he said. "After all, it's school holidays. We were all young once, too, and youngsters love an adventure. Let them go, meet other young people from all over the world and take heart."

Arrangements were made for the three youngsters to stay with Rosa's elderly parents in Moscow and off they went on the train, leaving Odessa Station with much excitement.

On their return from Moscow, they attended the next meeting of the group. They whispered enthusiastically about the Israeli delegates they had met. How happy and carefree they had seemed, how well they performed, how proud all the Russian Jews had felt!

"We met other Jews on the Odessa train," Yuri said, "who were on the same mission as we were. In fact, when we reached Moscow, there were thousands of Jews from all over the country who had come to see the Israeli delegates. They all cheered the Israeli team enthusiastically, looking for them in the streets of Moscow. The Moscow Jews invited them to their homes. We all begged for Israeli badges, booklets, matches and postcards."

Unbeknown to anyone else, seized by great emotion at seeing the young, proud Israeli athletes, Yossel had bought a Russian postcard, scribbled on it *'Im eshkachech Yerushalayim'*, 'If I forget thee, O Jerusalem', and handed it to the one male Israeli delegate who wore a *kippa* on his head. He saw the young man read the postcard and look amongst the throng for the writer. But Yossel, strongly aware of the KGB presence, and also embarrassed by his outburst of emotion, had quickly slipped back into the crowd.

Irina had a story to tell. "I met a man about 50 years old, who had travelled to Moscow all the way from Poland. He was one of the few Jews left in Poland. He told me he'd really believed in the Russian Revolution and communist ideology, hoping it would give us Jews a chance to live freely, without the threat of antisemitism. He worked for the Communist Party in Poland with great enthusiasm for many years, but now he feels devastated."

"He gave me a copy of a poem published this year in the Warsaw Yiddish Communist daily 'Folks-Shtimme'. It's written by Meir Kharatz and I think it puts into words the feelings of many Jews who've worked so hard for the Party and yet have never been truly accepted. Let me read this part to you...."

> *"Together we built here*
> *This house, like a song,*
> *But you, the original dwellers,*
> *Entered and locked the door.*
> *....I stand under the window,*
> *I rattle the window......"*

Chava mused to herself how the writing of poetry was a highly respected profession in Russia. A popular form of leisure activity was to spend an evening listening to poetry readings and Jews shared in this. She tried to remember which writer had said 'In the Soviet Union they take poetry very seriously - people get shot for it!'

Her mind wandered on. Yes, she thought, Jewish we are, but Russian too! Even when we have a celebration, we throw the guest of honour up in the air several times, just like Russian soldiers who have drunk too much vodka!

At least the children seem happy. It was a good idea to let them go, even if they stayed away much longer than intended. Thank goodness Yossel had kept his wits about him.

As a result of his early experiences, Yossel had developed a sixth sense with regard to possible danger. Wily as ever, he persuaded the others not to return to Odessa immediately, but to wait until the excitement had died down and railway stations were no longer being watched. He phoned Asher at work, to tell him of their decision.

In their own personal code, a trusted method used by millions of Soviet citizens to avoid real or imagined danger, Yossel informed Asher they would wait some time before venturing home.

"The Roads Are Dangerous, Asher. Besides, it's such fun being here. We're enjoying Moscow and doing a lot of sightseeing. We'll stay at least an extra week."

They arrived home from Moscow, disguised as peasants without informing their parents of their arrival as they didn't want to attract unwelcome attention.

By sensing the intention of the KGB, Yossel had probably saved their lives. By September, one hundred and twenty Jews had been sentenced to the notorious forced-labour camp of Vorkuta in Siberia for nine to seventeen years. Most were Moscow Jews who had entertained members of the Israeli delegation. The rest were Jews from other cities who had travelled to Moscow to meet the Israelis. Several thousand other Jews guilty of 'fraternisation' were removed, on various pretexts, from their jobs. Yes, Yossel, with his **acute understanding** of 'the enemy' had saved them.

CHAPTER FOURTEEN

A festering boil will eventually erupt. Kruschev was heard to say he didn't personally like the Jews, although one shouldn't call them Zids (or kikes) in public. Although Kruschev's antisemitism was not motivated by any political ideology, he did nothing to heal the festering boil of antisemitism in Russia and in fact either sanctioned or encouraged it.

Over the next few years, many of the Shuls which had previously avoided notice by the authorities, were closed down. Virulently antisemitic articles were again published.

Many of the newspaper articles and leaflets distributed throughout the Soviet Union were reminiscent of the Hitler's propaganda, certainly of the Stalin era.

It was frightening for the Aharonowitzes to see Jews depicted as ticks and parasites in the local newspaper, Znamya Kommunizma; Judaism described as a religion of hatred towards other religions and nations.

For the High Holidays of 1959, Yossel was asked to help with leading the service at the Brodska Sinagoga. On the morning of the Second Day of Rosh Hashanah, Natalya accompanied him on the forty-five minute walk to the Peressyp, while Asher and Chava attended the smaller *minyan* run by Chaim.

In the middle of Mussaf, hooligans ran into the Brodska synagogue shouting "Abrasha! Abrasha!" and attacked people at prayer. From the Bimah, Yossel's eyes immediately searched for Natalya. Although the attackers had not reached the ladies' section there was a look of fear and confusion on her face. His fierce feelings of protection towards Natalya overwhelmed him. He knew too this was one of the times that he should exact some revenge.

Unlike those of others who were too shocked and afraid to act, Yossel's blows and kicks were sharp and sure. As if he had prepared all his life for this moment, he shouted, "Fight for your life. Don't ask for favours, don't beg for mercy, just fight!" Seeing Yossel's courage and decisiveness, others gained strength, and it was not long before the attackers were chased out.

Yossel came home later that day like a wounded soldier. He was covered in cuts and bruises. As Chava bathed his wounds, tears came into her eyes and she quickly brushed them away to prevent him seeing them. But he had noticed them, and he looked at Chava openly.

"Don't cry, Chava," he said, softly, "it wasn't that bad. Natalya's safety was never threatened. And we got rid of them pretty quickly."

"I know," she answered, "I don't really know why I'm crying."

With his usual insight, Yossel gave her some understanding of herself. "You're crying because despite everything, you still long for peaceful times where we can continue with our lives without interference. You want to watch Natalya grow up into a happy young woman and you want me to forget about my past and create a simple uncomplicated future. Most of all, you don't want to see me resort to violence. It negates the spiritual nourishment on which you raised me."

"When did you learn to be so wise?" Chava said smiling through her tears.

Yossel didn't answer her. Instead he made her sit down, and looking at her directly, he said, "I solemnly swear to you, Chava, I'll never provoke or incite violence. Only if there is no alternative, as it was today, will I do what is necessary to defend myself and others."

To herself, Chava whispered, "Thank you, Almighty, for the healing and the strength that Yossel has gained in our home, together with the perspectives needed to live a balanced life."

A few days later, they heard the news that in the suburb of Malakhova, some fifteen miles southeast of Moscow, the small wooden Shul and the nearby cottage of the caretaker of the Jewish cemetery had been set ablaze. Firemen saved the Shul, but the nearby cottage was destroyed and the wife of the caretaker, seventy-year old Sarah Gordovskaya, perished in the blaze. Two antisemitic leaflets were found nearby.

All over the Soviet Union, different incidents had taken place, and the antisemitic feullitons and radio broadcasts grew in number and virulence. In December, Asher, Chava and Yossel sat aghast as they listened to the Odessa regional radio service. "The Jewish faith has been strongly intermixed with Jewish bourgeois nationalism and Zionism, already possessing a strong reactionary essence," the broadcaster was saying. "For such sermons are tools of the nationalistic, Israeli, cosmopolitan American bourgeoisie......... The Jews pray for the militant spirit of Israeli militarists....."

It was over this time that Asher fell into a serious depression. He lost his concentration, sleeping fitfully at night and waking up with nightmares of his labour camp experiences. He was irritable with everyone around him. Eventually, in a state of despair, Chava asked Chaim to come and chat to him. Perhaps he could pass some of his spiritual strength on to Asher.

When Chaim arrived, Chava left the living room and went to the kitchen. At first Chaim spoke quietly to Asher, trying gently to counter Asher's despair with words of hope in Hashem.

"Oh, please, Chaim!" Asher almost shouted. "You and I may speak of G-d, but we know the bulk of Soviet Jewry is lost to Judaism. Many of them have married out of our faith, most don't even know what the Torah is or even have a basic concept of any kind of religion.

"Look at us here in Odessa. The last census showed us we have about one hundred and eighty thousand Jews living here, as many as there were before the First World War. But we are a subdued people living in fear, trying to reduce our Jewishness to a minimum. We used to have eleven shuls with a membership of seventeen thousand congregants. All but one have been closed down. No Brises take place, no marriages under the Chupah. This community used to be vital, carefree and confident. Now it has no message to convey, no legacy to bequeath. It's no longer a great Jewish community."

"Let me tell you a story, my friend," Chaim said quietly. "There I am, sitting on the bus a few weeks ago. I see a young man looking at me intently. Oh ho, I say to myself, this must be KGB. There and then I decide to get off the bus so that if I'm caught, it won't be in the presence of Devorah and the children.

"The young man gets off the bus, too, and follows me. By now, I'm sure this is it. I'm thinking of how I can get a message to Devorah regarding my fate. At the same time, I'm thanking G-d that I at least have my Tehillim with me and I'm deciding how to hide it on my person. All kinds of thoughts are running through my head. I'm so grateful I've learnt so many Mishnayos off by heart, so that even if I'm placed in solitary confinement, I'll have my Talmud to learn. I'll not be bored.

"I'm tired of running from the authorities, tired even of being afraid, so I turn around and say to the young man bluntly, 'Can I help you, Comrade?'

"The poor man seems to be quite dumbfounded. And he starts to babble and stutter. Eventually, I offer him a seat on a bench we come across, and he tells me the following story.

" 'My parents never told me I was Jewish, and I never thought about it, but there were some incidents, some antisemitic incidents that took place at the University. I was specifically singled out. I went home and confronted my parents and they admitted to me that I am, in fact, Jewish by birth. I asked them what that meant but I was not given any meaningful answer. I see, by your dress, sir, and I say this respectfully, that you are Jewish, and I have come to ask you about Judaism. If I'm going to suffer all my life and be constantly pointed out as a Jew, then so be it, but at least let me understand what that means.'

"You can imagine I almost cried with joy and also with relief. I invited him to come to our home for Shabbos and began teaching him the *aleph beis* and the very rudiments of Judaism, as Devorah's father did for you many years ago. The end of quite a long story is that I now have ten students whom I teach in secret twice a week. It has added such joy to our lives. Even the children know our secret because it gives us all hope here in this spiritual darkness.

"Do you know what I think? The Soviet government has made the biggest mistake it could have with the Jewish people. If it had just left the Jews alone, they would have all happily assimilated. But because they have been so kind as to keep reminding us who we are, a lot of the youngsters are saying, 'Well, if I've got to be a Jew, then let me be a Jew - and be proud of it!'

"And let me tell you something else. In his Yomtov wishes to us, Aharon wrote he and his father are very busy with their 'work.' You and I know that for Uncle Dov and Aharon, they only regard the teaching of Torah as their 'work.' I believe if Torah learning and awakening is happening in suburbs of Odessa and Kiev it is happening all over the Soviet Union."

Asher stared at Chaim with disbelief. "Baruch Hashem," he kept saying over and over again, "Baruch Hashem. There is a reason to hope!" And his depression slowly lifted.

CHAPTER FIFTEEN

The time was fast approaching when Yossel and Yuri would complete their schooling. Both Yossel and Yuri were excellent students, and stood a good chance of achieving A aggregates for their final examinations. They attended the dance which was always held at the school during the last term of the students' final year. Together with the others they stayed and enjoyed the festivities until the early hours of the morning when students from all over Odessa met at Nikolaevsky Boulevard to watch the sunrise.

One of the great achievements of communism in the Soviet Union was its success in creating many varied institutions of learning, both at basic and higher levels. To a large extent, this eradicated the illiteracy and ignorance of the masses that existed before the Revolution. Odessa, like most of the larger cities, boasted many higher institutions of learning. There was the Mechnikov University as well as fifteen Institutes of Technology and two Music Conservatories.

All universities in the Soviet Union were run on a strict quota system, whereby only a certain number of people from each national group was allowed to be accepted. Because the Jewish quota was so low, it was virtually impossible to gain entrance unless one's parents knew someone in authority who would assist the candidate with his request.

Irina had not been accepted at the Odessa university two years earlier. But Sasha, however, who was acquainted with one of the deans of students from his army days, managed to arrange her entrance to Moscow University. Irina boarded with Rosa's parents. She was enjoying her studies and was delighted to be spending time with her elderly grandparents.

Yuri, with his great love for the violin, was thrilled to be accepted at the Nizhdanova Conservatory of Music in Odessa. There were many young Jews there, although some would never admit to being Jewish, and he found both excitement and a measure of contentment in his life of music and learning.

With his creative and academic abilities Yossel began to study architecture at the Institute of Civil Engineering. His ideal was to provide homes for people that were both functional and beautiful. Aside from his secular learning, there was always the Talmud to turn to for spiritual upliftment.

Once Yossel and Yuri had left school to join institutes of higher learning, they stopped coming to the regular family meetings. Both were proud of their Jewish identity. Yossel made it clear he was observant and would not desecrate the Sabbath or festivals, even to write examinations. Yuri, although not fully observant, always wore a cap or kippa, his tiny act of pride and defiance.

Both young men were amazed to find other Jewish students approaching them after studies and begging to be taught in secret. "I want to learn something about Judaism - my parents don't know enough to help me," said one girl to Yossel. "Can you teach me Hebrew?" a young man asked Yuri. All expressed a desire to learn more about Israel.

So it was that Yossel and Yuri formed their own illegal group in Odessa. Yossel taught the basics of Judaism. They managed to find an older man who was happy to teach them Hebrew, and they all shared snippets of information about Israel.

One would tell what he had heard on the latest broadcasts of Kol Yisrael Lagolah - The Voice of Israel to the Diaspora - when that radio station was not jammed by the authorities. Yossel would read the latest letter received from his Uncle Pinchas in Israel. One of the girls would teach them an Israeli dance she had learned from 'a friend'. The friend was reluctant to disclose the name of the person from whom she had learned it.

No-one really understood the slowly rising tide of interest in Jewish matters by the young Jewish people of the Soviet Union. They themselves never realised the extent of it. Over the years during which the flame of Judaism was rekindled, it is almost certain the various groups in Odessa were unaware of others in the city. It is probable they were totally unaware of the burgeoning groups in Kiev, Riga, Moscow and other centres.

Perhaps it was the freedom from Stalin's reign of terror. Perhaps it was the easing of the authorities' attitude towards communication between Russians and the outside world. The occasional Jewish visitors from abroad, particularly from Israel, gave the young people hope and a sense of connection with their people all over the world. These visitors could never comprehend the fear that seemed to encompass the Jews when they entered the Soviet Union.

Or perhaps it was the strange *'davka'* streak in people making them long for what is denied to them.

Certainly, the authorities helped the flame to grow by their antisemitic and insensitive activities. When

Uncle Dov came to visit Devorah, Chaim and eight grandchildren in the middle of 1961, he told a gruesome yet uplifting story.

"Remember," he said, "how the Jews of Kiev gather in the valley of Babi Yar every Tisha B'Av, to honour the memory of the hundred thousand Jews who were slaughtered there by Germans and Ukrainians on Yom Kippur, 1942?" Chaim and Devorah nodded.

They all knew the city council of Kiev did everything in its power to prevent these gatherings, on one occasion even sending police to block the roads. "This year," he went on, "despite protests from Jews, a residential area called the Podol was built on the lower slopes of the ravine.

"The worst happened a few months ago when the City Council announced a plan to build a sports stadium and park on the valley floor of Babi Yar where so many of our relatives are buried. A dance pavilion was planned - right in the centre.

"All the angry protests of Jewish organizations were ignored. But the Almighty must have heard their cries of anguish. For one morning, before any building had begun, there was a tremendous cloudburst over the Podol causing a huge mudslide which buried the entire Podol and killed thousands of people."

Chaim and Devorah shook their heads in disbelief. "The morning after the disaster," Uncle Dov continued, "I went out to see Babi Yar. There I came across a very devout and pious young woman whose six brothers had been murdered at Babi Yar. Her name was Devorah Meislik. She worked night shift as an accountant and had been on the last streetcar to make its way safely through the Podol just before the cloudburst.

"Together we gazed in horror and awe at the skulls and bones of our fellow Jews floating everywhere in a sea of mud. Since that time, since the bones of the dead of Babi Yar rose to the surface, no more has been heard about building a sports stadium and dance pavilion in Babi Yar."

When Devorah told this story to Chava, Chava was overwhelmed. "Isn't it amazing," she mused, "when one sees evidence of heavenly intervention?"

When Yossel began his studies at the Institute, Natalya was in her sixth year and started her formal schooling. She had Chava's blonde hair, but Asher's olive skin and brown eyes. No quiet beauty, she was very talkative and had an enquiring mind.

When she came home with communist ideology and atheist beliefs from school, she challenged them all with questions. She wanted to understand on what basis her father, mother and Yossel could possibly believe in a G-d one could not see and in a faith that was ancient and outmoded.

For years, she tested their patience and love. She told them she was not prepared to risk her life and record of good conduct at school by refusing to write on Shabbos. When it became forbidden to bake *matzah*, Chava went to help Devorah, but Natalya refused. She wanted nothing to do with it.

The usual pre-Pesach discussion took place between Asher and Chava. "Tell me again, Pappa," Natalya asked, "why do we eat matzah on Pesach?"

"Because we're instructed to do so, in the Torah."

"Who wrote the Torah?"

"The Ribbono Shel Olam wrote the Torah."

"How do you know that G-d exists?"

At this question, Asher would smile. "It's a leap of faith, Nechamele, which I hope one day you will feel able to make. In the meantime, believe me, the Jewish way of life is a very sensible religion which has many advantages and brings great joy. Try to practise whatever you can and trust that the faith will come later."

Chaim and Devorah began their *matzah* preparations about sixty days before Pesach. The day before Tu Bishevat, they bought wheat from a farmer and checked through the wheat. Each kernel was individually inspected for signs of swelling, which would indicate it had begun to sprout and become *chametz*.

They bought a large amount of wheat to supply not only their own needs but also the needs of a few religious families, and many others who held a vestige of Jewish tradition - the desire to taste a piece of *matzah* on Pesach.

The day after Purim, with the checking finished, Chaim and Devorah drove out to the village where they had bought the wheat and looked for a farmer who worked at the mill. Asher and Devorah helped to pay this farmer the hefty price he requested for taking off the millstones, removing all traces of flour, and then grinding their *shemurah* wheat.

The actual baking of the *matzos* took several days. Chaim and Devorah's children would enjoy the task of running the 'redler', a toothed wheel, all over each *matzah* just before it went into the oven. The little holes it made kept the *matzah* from puffing up during baking. Chava was heartbroken that Natalya showed no desire to help and be part of the excitement.

Aside from the huge amount of work involved, the home baking of *matzah* was an almost heroic undertaking, because the baking and the sale of *matzah* often led to arrests on the grounds of either religious coercion or on the grounds of 'economic crimes'.

'Economic crimes' covered those such as the independent production of goods using materials stolen or illegally purchased, their sale on the black market, dealing in precious stones and foreign currency; and offering or accepting bribes.

Between 1961 and 1964 special prominence was given in the media when the accused were Jews. The newspaper reports often turned the trials into show pieces. If the family name of the accused did not sound Jewish, his first name and that of his father would be given in full and the press had no qualms about denigrating the accused.

There were official denials, some of them by Khrushchev himself, that the economic trials were anti-Jewish, but it was clear there was an anti-Jewish policy at that time. It seems the authorities were using antisemitism to disguise economic problems thereby directing general dissatisfaction away from the leadership.

These problems did not seem to affect Natalya. As a little girl not yet ten years old, she stood with the people of The Motherland, on her own, connected yet disconnected from her family, and she caused them much grief and heartache.

CHAPTER SIXTEEN

Chava and Asher would often marvel at the passage of time and at how quickly the younger generation were growing up.

"We're getting old," Chava would say with a smile to Asher. "I remember my parents talking about how quickly the years had flown and how we'd grown up overnight. Now it's our turn to be doing the same."

Although they were proud of Yossel and Natalya, they worried about both of them. Natalya was often sweet and co-operative at home. Nevertheless, most of the time she refused to participate in any religious activities. It was during those times that Asher would comfort Chava saying, "Give her time to grow up. I was the same at her age. We don't have to despair."

Yossel, they were all sure, was under constant KGB surveillance. He was a genius at keeping one step ahead of the authorities and not being caught doing any illegal activity. But it seemed he lived in a state of apprehension, prepared for imminent arrest.

The family, too, prepared themselves psychologically. Every day, when he went off to work, Chava would put a few tins of food in his lunch box and some dried fruit, just in case 'he might be held up late, stay out longer than expected'. Asher and Yossel tried to devise a code whereby they could send each other messages indirectly.

Having somewhat made his peace with the horror of his years in Siberia, Asher now took to speaking at length about his experiences in the camps, giving pointed hints to Yossel. "The one thing one had to hold on to, all the way, even on the trains travelling between the camps, was one's bowl. It seems such a silly thing now. But if you lost your bowl, or obeyed the guards when they told you to hand it in, you were in such a serious predicament when hot gruel or porridge was handed out, and of course, water."

"Yes, yes!" he would carry on. "In the trains you have to choose your bunk cleverly. In the winter time, it's best to grab a bottom bunk, next to the stove. In the summer time, of course, you try for one of the upper bunks near the window."

Chava's heart would contract with pain for what her husband had endured, and with fear for what Yossel might have to suffer. Still, they all prayed, that with G-d's help and Yossel's astuteness when it came to dealing with the authorities, he would somehow remain safe.

In June, 1965, Chava noticed a change in Yossel. He walked around with a slight swagger, took great care with his appearance and every now and then he had a dreamy look in his eyes.

Chava suspected Yossel was in love, but she did not question him. However, one Thursday evening, which was balmy and warm, he sat down at the kitchen table while Chava was preparing food for Shabbos.

"Do we have any guests coming for Shabbos?" he asked.

"Yes, Sasha, Rosa and Irina are coming. You remember, Irina's home for the holidays, and we're all going to be together again."

Chava stopped and looked at him. "Is there anyone else you would like to ask, Yossel? We can always make room for one or two more, you know that."

Yossel was hesitant. "Well, there's a girl who comes to our group now. She grew up in an orphanage and she's a little different, not always at ease with people. She believes she's Jewish and has become obsessed with learning about Judaism. She has demanded I spend extra time teaching her and wants to try to practise everything."

"Bring her!" said Chava quickly. Her own childhood, the fact that she had been orphaned at such a young age, made her heart go out to what sounded like a lonely, lost soul. "We'll be happy to have her."

The evening was a great success, the young people all enjoying each other's company. The others, relaxed for once, savouring the easy conversation and laughter of old friends.

During the meal, Irina told everyone of the amazing occurrence that had started taking place in Moscow outside the Shul at Archipova Street.

"It started off just happening on Simchas Torah," she explained. "Thousands and thousands of Jews, especially young Jews, Jews who have never prayed before and don't know what a Torah is, come to sing and dance or even just to stand outside the Shul. Now it happens several times during the year. It would be worthwhile coming to visit Moscow just to see this wonderful event."

"Can I go, Mama? Could I maybe go to Moscow for Simchas Torah?" Natalya asked.

"But we have our own large crowds here in Odessa these days and our own singing and dancing," laughed Chava.

"Yes, but it sounds even better in Moscow!" exclaimed Natalya. "Please, please let me go to Moscow for Succos," she begged.

Chava looked at Asher, amazed when he replied, "We'll see, Nechamele. Perhaps we'll make a visit to Moscow your Basmitzvah present."

Chava just shook her head, thinking to herself it was still a long time to Sukkos. She could argue about it later. She tried to concentrate her efforts on the newcomer.

Yossel had introduced his friend as Bas-sheva. She seemed to be a self-conscious young lady. She had a round figure and sat a little hunched, but she smiled constantly at everyone and her eyes seemed to shine throughout the evening.

When the Dubnowitzes had left, Asher and Chava spent a little time with Bas-sheva, wanting to know and understand her, as it was clear that Yossel had set his heart on her.

"We hope you enjoyed yourself, my dear," Asher said to her.

"Oh yes," she said softly, "thank you, it was one of the best evenings of my life. I felt as if I was with family. When one grows up in an orphanage, one always feels deprived of family life. And then too, there were all the wonderful Jewish customs, songs and prayers. I had Yossel here explaining everything to me. It was truly wonderful."

"Do you know anything about your family, Bas-sheva?" Asher asked her.

With a hint of sadness in her eyes, she began, "No, nothing. It's terrible not to know where you come from, who your parents were, whether you ever had brothers and sisters. I was found on a train line, on the tracks when I was about four or five months old.

There was a note pinned onto my little coat which said 'Bas-sheva Feldman, daughter of Akiva and Rochel Feldman, who died in the bombing of Odessa. Please take care of this precious child'."

Chava had gone white and sat down. In disbelief, she began to weep and laugh at the same time. "It's you, it's....Bashi," she said over and over again.

"What, that Bashi, that you always dream about?" asked Asher.

"Yes, yes, the same Bashi," laughed Chava breathlessly. "Oh, my dear, do you mind if I hug you?"

Bas-sheva incredulously allowed herself to be hugged and then she and Yossel begged Chava to explain herself.

Until the early hours of the morning, Chava spoke of her brief time with Bashi during the early days of the war. She tried to remember every detail that might be recorded in her memory. The sandwich and coffee offered to her by Bashi's kindly mother, when Chava was feeling sad and desolate. The comfort offered by the Feldmans when Chava and her parents were devastated at the loss of Maish. She tried to describe how they looked, how mischievous and sweet Bashi's brothers were.

Chava also described the terrible night of bombing in the Malakhova district of Odessa, and her finding baby Bashi alive but cold, shocked and hungry. She and Bashi were the sole survivors of their families.

They worked out that Bashi's uncle and aunt were probably put on a transport to a concentration camp and that on the way, they may have tried to save their younger children and Bashi by putting them through a hole made in their carriage, dropping them on the train line and praying they would be found and saved before being run over by the next train. It was a chance they took, and with Bashi, it had worked.

Bas-sheva, who was now Bashi for everybody, stayed the entire Shabbos. She was totally overwhelmed and kept close to Chava, asking her questions. "Was my mother fat or thin, short or tall?" she asked.

"She was small and round like you. I think you have her warm, green eyes," Chava replied.

"And your parents were religious, much more than my parents were. They demonstrated great kindness and warmth. And your mother had such a peace and calmness about her despite the circumstances in which we all found ourselves."

"I feel as if I've just found my roots, my home!" Bashi blurted out. "Yossel, tell me, isn't there a blessing to say when you're feeling grateful and happy?"

"Well," he replied, with a warm smile on his face, "you could say 'Hodu Ladoshem Ki Tov, Ki Leolam Chasdo' Give thanks to G-d for He is good, because His kindness endures forever!"

It wasn't only Bashi who felt moved to say this blessing. Chava said it aloud, supposedly to teach Bashi, but also with gratitude to the Almighty for finding Bashi alive after so many years.

Asher said it softly to himself, as he saw in Bashi the perfect wife for his nephew, Yossel. Bashi and Yossel both held deep scars from the period of the war. They would be able to help and understand each other. Hashem had helped Yossel to find his *basherte* - his destined one.

Yossel said the blessing because he was very happy and in love and because Asher and Chava seemed to like the girl he had chosen.

And Natalya, of her own accord, whispered the prayer to herself, because for once their family had been filled with joy, all fears forgotten. Yossel and Bashi looked like they were going to get married - and Pappa had said there was a chance she could go to Moscow for Succos.   Hodu Ladoshem Ki Tov Ki Leolam Chasdo!

CHAPTER SEVENTEEN

For the first time in years, a Jewish wedding was planned in Odessa - under a Chupah in the Shul. Nobody felt totally at ease about it.

In the first place, Yossel and Bashi had applied for exit visas to Israel. Both had been turned down and lost their jobs as a result. They no longer attended any meetings, afraid to jeopardise the safety of the other members. They lived an almost twilight existence, Yossel struggling to find casual work each day to avoid being picked up by the authorities for being a parasite.

In the second place, the reaction to ritual observance by the authorities was still somewhat erratic. Sometimes it was condoned. At other times there were harsh punishments. One never knew what to expect.

Nevertheless, Chava, with all the fear she held in her heart, could not help feeling excited and happy. There were so many people she wanted to invite to share their joy - Devorah, Chaim and their eight children, the Dubnowitzes, the Rochinskys and Asher's friends. She planned a little party for afterwards - a big pot of borscht with hot potatoes, a variety of cold fish and salads and a few cakes and coffee. If it was not impossible, she would buy some fruits on the black market.

But as the wedding drew near, she noticed an agitation about Yossel and Bashi. Bashi moved into their home and slept in the kitchen. They both spoke briefly about meetings with contacts, but gave no details.

One evening, a week before the wedding was due to take place, after Natalya had gone to sleep, Yossel and Bashi asked to speak to Asher and Chava.

"Asher, Chava, what we have to say to you is very difficult," began Asher. "We both feel certain that within the next few days, perhaps even tonight, we'll be arrested, probably for Zionist activities."

"We have two things to tell you. The first is that we must arrange to have the Chupa as soon as we can, tomorrow night in fact. We're so afraid of being arrested before we are married, and being sent to different camps, perhaps never seeing each other again."

"The other thing is...the other thing is... we're going to try to escape from Russia - tomorrow."

Chava gasped and sat down. Asher clasped his chest and began coughing, that usual bronchial cough, which often came on unexpectedly.

Chava glanced at Asher and saw he could not speak. "What have you planned?" she whispered to the young couple.

Yossel sighed, obviously overwrought. "Our people in Israel and the rest of the world are finally trying to help us. There are two men in Odessa. They have Hungarian passports, but they're actually from Israel, sent by the Jewish Agency."

"The plan is that tomorrow night, after the wedding, Bashi and I will board a Cuban ship in the harbour. The Jewish Agency have bribed the captain to help us stowaway on board, protect us and drop us off at their next stop, Izmir in Turkey. At Izmir, we hope to be met by other members of the Jewish Agency, who will give us Israeli documents and accompany us to Istanbul. From Istanbul, we take a boat to Cyprus, and from Cyprus a ferry to Israel."

Asher finally forced himself to speak. "This all seems so uncertain, Yossel." He coughed again. "What if you are let down on the other side and nobody comes to meet you?"

Yossel clenched and unclenched his fists. There was a deep frown on his forehead and he was biting his lips. Chava could see he was nervous. The bravado he'd displayed for years had disappeared. While he continued to be fearless on his own behalf, he was desperate to protect Bashi from all harm.

"We have no option but to try, Asher," he said hesitantly. "At worst, we'll reach Turkey. If no-one is there to meet us, we'll have to act like tourists, try to find some temporary work to support ourselves, and ultimately make our own way to Israel."

There was nothing further to be said. Asher and Chava had to adjust to the new plan as soon as possible, adjust to Yossel and Bashi's leaving just as their arms and souls were joyfully reaching out to widen the family circle.

Chava was in shock, but she tried to hide it for everybody else's sake. She accompanied Bashi to the secret Mikva at Chaim and Devorah's house, smiled gaily when the ritual was over. She welcomed Yuri and Chaim to their home when they arrived later to act as witnesses to the marriage ceremony. She assisted the Rabbi to set up a makeshift canopy, a pretty tablecloth, tied one corner to the handle of a tall kitchen cupboard, the other three corners being held by Asher, Yuri and Chaim.

During the hurried ceremony, somewhat tinged with fear, she allowed herself to relax a little and just savour the moment. Her eyes clouded over and she imagined them all in the big Shul at Peressyp, surrounded by their friends. Ah, see, they were now at the reception in their apartment. Everyone was laughing, singing and dancing. People were complimenting her on the food she had spent days preparing. There was no terror here, just pure joy.

Her reverie stopped abruptly when Yossel stamped on the glass. What? Over so soon? It couldn't be! The Rabbi was wishing them all *mazeltov*, putting on his coat and preparing to leave - quickly - away from this house of danger and suspicion.

Yuri was holding both of Yossel's hands in his. There was a glint of tears in his eyes but he smiled bravely. "See you soon," he whispered hoarsely, and with a wink at Bashi he, too, was at the door. "Let me know, please, as soon as you know, Uncle Asher," he said as he made his way out, and then he too, was gone.

Chava felt Natalya's arms around her. Natalya had grown up that night knowing she had to be a support to her parents.

But Chaim stayed for a cup of coffee and a piece of cake. He stayed while Yossel and Bashi went to the bedroom and feverishly put on Cuban sailors' uniforms. Bashi tied up her hair and tucked it well under her cap. They packed small bags, placed their internal Russian passports behind the bookcase and put their new forged Cuban documents in their pockets. And he stayed while tearful goodbyes were said.

When Yossel shook his hand, he murmured softly to him, "Avraham Avinu also had a dangerous journey to the land of Israel, as did our other forefathers. They all went through great trials and perils, but they believed in Hashem's guidance and protection and they ended their journeys safely. So may it be with you!"

The others could not speak any more as they were too pent-up with emotion. Yossel managed to blurt out, "I will leave messages with Aharon in Kiev. For anyone else, it will be too dangerous."

However many times they hugged each other, it did not seem enough. How does one say goodbye forever?

In the end, it was Chaim who gently steered Yossel and his sweet bride to the door.

After they had left, Chaim declared he was very thirsty again. "Come! It's time now for a glass of black tea!" he declared, lighting the stove himself.

Chaim stayed till late that night, encouraging them all, talking about faith, about the wonderful future of freedom and Torah assured to Yossel and Bashi. Finally, he too had to take his leave. And then the three of them were left alone.

They all forced themselves up the next morning, to get to work, to get to school, to act normally, so no-one would suspect anything unusual. Asher made his way down to the harbour the following day during his lunch break and was grateful to find the Cuban freighter had left.

Before dawn the next day, they were awoken by a loud knocking. None of them needed to be told who it was. The KGB searched everywhere, throwing the apartment into disarray, but those they had come for had left.

The questioning went on for hours. The answers were repeated many times. Yes, the couple had married, by Jewish Law. Yes, they'd gone away on honeymoon. No, they refused to tell where they were going. They were anxious to run off, but they would register their marriage with the authorities in Odessa as soon as they arrived home. Again, no, they had told no-one of their whereabouts. But try Sebastopol, where lots of the young couples go.

The secret police left angry and perturbed some hours later. Asher knew they felt certain they would catch the young couple sooner or later.

A feeling almost of elation overwhelmed him. "Oh, no, my friends, not this time," he wanted to shout at them.

Their apartment continued to be watched for months on end, but it hardly bothered them, for just two weeks after Yossel and Bashi left, Aharon phoned from Kiev to say a telegram had come from Uncle Pinchas in Israel. The two parcels had arrived intact, in excellent condition.

And with this they had to be satisfied.

CHAPTER EIGHTEEN

Initially it was Natalya who tried to be cheerful
for them all. She made jokes about finally being able
to sleep on Yossel's sofa in the living room, instead of
behind the partition in her parents' room. She had a
wide circle of friends ranging from Chaim and
Devorah's third child, Esther, to gentile friends from
her class. But she avoided them, coming home to
chatter, laugh and tell silly jokes, as if making enough
noise for two or three would fill the empty spaces in
Asher and Chava's hearts.

They understood this and loved her all the more
for it. As time passed, her parents in their adult
fashion came to terms with Yossel and Bashi's
absence. The news from the young couple was good.
In the coded letters which finally began to arrive at
their front door instead of at Aharon's, Yossel and
Bashi spoke about an Ulpan at Netanya, where their
Hebrew had greatly improved. A baby was on the
way. They were amazed at a world of freedom and
choices hitherto denied them.

Knowledge of the children's contentment was a
comfort to Asher and Chava. But as the months
dragged on, Natalya began to miss Yossel and Bashi's
presence desperately. Yossel had always been her
protector, hero and friend. And in the short time she
had known Bashi, Natalya had quickly begun to look
upon her as a sister. The feeling had been mutual, for

lonely Bashi had been delighted to find a ready-made family welcoming her into their circle.

As time passed and the realisation dawned on Natalya she would probably never see Yossel and Bashi again, a sadness overwhelmed her she could neither hide nor contain. It was for this reason, when some youngsters a few years older than Natalya invited her to join them on a trip to Moscow for Simchas Torah, her parents encouraged her to go, despite their fears. Irina and her new husband, Yosef, promised to take care of her, and so the young lady went off to Moscow for Succot.

Chava was so apprehensive while Natalya was away, she could not sleep at all. She threw a little 'party' when Natalya returned safe and well, inviting the regular group and their children as well as the Gutsteins, so everyone could hear about Simchat Torah in Moscow.

Chava was amazed at how Natalya sat in the centre of the group, her back erect, her voice clear, a little ambassadress from Moscow. She answered their questions eloquently.

"So, how do things seem for the Jews of Moscow?" one person asked.

"Like it is for us," Natalya answered. "One still sees fear in their eyes. During Succot and Shemini Atzeret, the Shul in Archipova Street contained mostly old people. There were very few my age and younger who attended the service. But on Simchas Torah, everything was different!"

Chava watched as Natalya entranced everyone with her story.

"Yes, everything was different. Irina and I estimated there were about forty thousand Jews there, and none of them seemed afraid."

Natalya's eyes were sparkling. "The *hakafot* went on till two o'clock in the morning and even then despite the biting cold and frost in the air, nobody wanted to go home. People were singing and dancing. In the Shul, I saw an old man with his grandson on his shoulders push his way through the crowds towards one of the men carrying a Torah, and say, 'Kiss the Torah, little one,' and the grandson complied. Like our children here, the children in Moscow do not know what a Torah is, but they were excited by the feelings of joy and identity aroused."

"Did you see visitors from Israel or other countries?" Yuri wanted to know.

Natalya smiled and answered quickly, "Oh yes, of course. For the first *hakafah*, Rabbi Levin and all the *gabbaim* were given the honour of carrying the Torot. Then the guests from abroad were given the honour. But they couldn't move. Everybody broke out in song - different songs. From one group 'Heiveinu shalom aleichem'. From another group 'David Melech Yisrael'. The Muscovites all rushed forward to surround them, touch them, whisper blessings or entreaties in their ears."

Natalya blushed a little. "I couldn't help myself. I rushed forward to one of the Israeli tourists and said to him, 'My brother Yossel and his wife Bashi live in Jerusalem!' "

"And what did he reply?" everyone asked.

"He gave me a big smile, and said 'Gam ani' - me too. And before he had time to say anything else, an old man grabbed him by his coat and said, 'Tell them in Israel that despite everything that has happened, the Jews of Russia have not forgotten their heritage. They must not forget us.' "

Chava noticed tears in the eyes of many of the adults present.

Natalya continued, "Irina and I were feeling so hot inside the Shul then, we were almost fainting. We had to go out. What a sight awaited us there! Thousands of Jews, young and old, singing, dancing, playing guitars - of course, they don't know about Yom Tov - or just milling around."

"I can't begin to describe everything to you. Irina had showed me some of the sights a few days before. The Kremlin was just ten minutes away, echoes of the celebration could reach the tomb of Stalin. Jews, mostly young Jews, were singing Yiddish and Hebrew songs, dancing Israeli folk dances, tossing their friends into the air, Russian style, absolutely shouting about their Jewishness!"

"I saw a man ask one of the Israeli tourists for an Israeli flag. As he was handing it over, an informer tried to stop them. But the Russian Jew just glared at him and he slunk away. Yes! Archipova Street was ours for the night."

The questions and the chatter went on and on, even while Chava served cake and hot steaming tea to warm everyone before they departed into the freezing night air. Nobody wanted to go home. Everybody wanted to stay and hear a little more, another anecdote from Natalya's Simchat Torah in Moscow.

Since Natalya's safe arrival home, Chava had been able to sleep with ease again. But that night she tossed restlessly in her bed.

Why, she asked herself. It seems at last Natalya has found G-d and her people. We felt so proud of her. She was at ease speaking to all the visitors, young and old. She spoke confidently and eloquently, filling her audience with awe, excitement and hope.

Aha! There it was. That new feeling of anxiety for Natalya. When she was tiny, we worried about her health. Every cough and sneeze frightened us. When she grew older, we worried that she did not care for her heritage. Now we know, Baruch Hashem, that she is totally dedicated, and will use her dedication to inspire others. Heaven help us! Is she, too, doomed to a life of danger and fear in the Soviet Union, like Yossel?

CHAPTER NINETEEN

Yes, she was. Ten years later, Chava would look back on Natalya's growing strength and leadership. Her poised courtroom appearance as a religious Jewess and refusenik had almost killed Asher.

Finally, when Natalya was sentenced to hard labour in Siberia at the age of twenty, Asher gave up the struggle against his chest problems, contracted double pneumonia and died.

After Asher passed away, there were many days when Chava could hardly bring herself to get up in the morning. Despite her faith, she thought of ending it all, unable to bear her grief for Asher, and her longing for her absent children. Apart from missing her daughter, there was the constant anxiety over whether Natalya would survive her ten-year sentence.

Oh, she was no longer young, no longer had what it took to keep going against all odds. There were letters of support and encouragement from others. Most appreciated were those received from a brave lady called Ida Nudel, who kept up the spirits of refuseniks and their families, sacrificing her own freedom and good health to do so.

And truly, the Dubnowitzes were wonderfully kind. So were Sasha and Rosa, until they returned to Moscow to be near Irina and her husband and help with the grandchildren. Even Yuri and his young wife often visited.

But in the early seventies, Chaim, Devorah and their family, together with their married children and grandchildren, were all given permission to leave. This was another tremendous blow for Chava, although she was delighted for them. She had always so relied on them as a source of spiritual strength. After their departure, during some of her worst hours of loneliness and doubt, she longed for their moral courage and conviction, and had to search for these deep within herself.

Uncle Dov, despite being on his deathbed after a severe stroke, insisted they go. He died in Kiev, in Aharon's home, in many ways a contented man. For he had spent his life doing what he thought G-d expected of him, and was secure in the knowledge that his surviving children and grandchildren were following in his footsteps.

Once, after repeated requests, she was given permission to visit Natalya at her camp in Siberia. How she prepared for the journey! She tried to remember Asher's hints to Yossel. Would Natalya need a new bowl, a new mug? By now her clothes must have worn through. She would give Natalya her coat. She could wear Asher's old one.

She was sure Asher had mentioned the need for books and games like draughts and chess to feed the spirits. Well, she would pack some of these, as well as some food and special treats for Natalya.

How long and frightening the journey was, especially when, close to Siberia, she was picked up, taken into custody by the police and questioned for days. Refused permission to travel any further and summarily placed on a train back home, she thought her heart would break, that she could bear no more.

All the way back to Odessa, in an effort to alleviate her own despair, she focussed on the amazing phenomenon taking place amongst Russian Jewry. How had it happened that religious feeling had been rekindled among so many people after three generations of atheist indoctrination? After all, many Jews had been at the forefront of the Communist revolution, happy to discard all beliefs and trappings.

Was it because of the devotion of people like Uncle Dov and his children? Was it because of the Jews from abroad who smuggled in *siddurim* and *tefillin* and taught Torah in secret on their brief visits to the country. She didn't know.

Had there always been a love for Israel? Yes, always. Why, in Lithuania before the war, there had been active, vibrant Zionist groups. And her father had spoken of the famous Zionists and Hebraists who had lived in Odessa, her adopted city.

All she knew was that after the Six-Day War in Israel in June 1967, there was a burgeoning pride in Jewish identity, even among those who had not previously involved themselves in Jewish affairs. What followed was a wave of interest in Judaism and a yearning to leave the Soviet Union and go to Israel.

The authorities did everything they could to contain this wave, spreading propaganda about Israel in the newspapers, arresting members of the secret and not-so-secret groups. They insisted to the world that the Jews of the Soviet Union were contented and happy and had no desire to go anywhere else.

But they were not successful. The Jews of Russia knew full well the small State of Israel had conquered the armies of five Arab countries - countries supported by the arms and military intelligence of the mighty Soviet Union. So how could the newspapers talk of Israel as a land of discontented, deprived people?

The people who made up the Zionist and Jewish study groups were now sure of themselves, sure of what they wanted to achieve in this world, and so when some were arrested, they had the open support of the others. They were no longer alone.

Perhaps, more important than anything, world Jewry had at long last declared support for their brothers and sisters in the Soviet Union and were gathering together in world centres like Jerusalem and Washington to shout 'Let my people go!'

Word reached the young Jews of Russia that on Passover, Jewish families all over the world had left an empty seat at their Seder tables for 'the Russian Jews' who were not free to celebrate the festival as they were, and were not permitted to leave their country.

Barmitzvah boys had their names linked to a Pavel, Grigory or Alexander - from Leningrad, Kiev or Riga - who were not able to celebrate this occasion freely in the Soviet Union. The family of the Barmitzvah boys would leave an empty chair in their midst. There would be a sign with the boy's name affixed to the seat, and a *tallit* hanging over it. In his speech, the Barmitzvah boy of the free world would mention his counterpart in Russia. In many different ways and in many different languages he was saying 'We stand with you. You are no longer alone.'

World pressure eventually played its part in alleviating the plight of Soviet Jews.

Natalya was released in 1977, after three years in Siberia. When she arrived home, Chava could see that despite the cold, the hunger and general wretchedness of her life in Siberia, Natalya had grown into a beautiful young woman. Foolishly, the authorities had placed all the political prisoners together. And so the refuseniks were able to encourage and fortify each other.

A young man was at Natalya's side, whom, against all odds, she had met and married during her imprisonment. His name was Lev Kagan. Tall and blonde, a peaked cap on his head, he looked typically Russian. But his appearance was deceptive for he shared Natalya's burning faith and rebellious spirit.

The couple were given two weeks to make use of the exit visa granted to them. Lev's mother had passed away but his father and brother came down from Minsk for a brief reunion - and to bid him farewell.

The authorities still maintained their ultimate cruelty, however, by denying Chava her exit visa when she requested it. Yet she insisted Natalya and Lev should leave. When Natalya wept at the thought of abandoning her widowed mother, Chava tried to think what Chaim and Devorah would have said. "To G-d nothing is impossible. If He wants the Jews of Russia to go free, he will do it just like that!" And she snapped her fingers. "There can never be any peace for Jews in the Soviet Union. Of that I feel certain. You must go."

CHAPTER TWENTY

Alone for thirteen years, with only Marina and Eli left for company, Chava filled her lonely hours by teaching Hebrew. She also gave lessons in Jewish studies and helped to organise camps for children where they could learn about their heritage.

Chava never knew exactly when Perestroika started. She didn't even know the date when it became official that Jews wishing to leave the Soviet Union to emigrate to Israel were now allowed to do so. She only knew that for the first time in many years she could let herself dream of seeing her children and grandchildren in Israel.

Chaim and Bashi lived in Jerusalem with their six children. Natalya and Lev now had eight children. Throughout the long years of waiting, Natalya would send letters describing almost every detail of their lives in the Galilee, in a newly-built town called Ma'agan Michael. In every letter Natalya would say, 'We are waiting for you, Mamma. I constantly tell the children that their Bobba from Odessa longs to see them.' Photographs of all the grandchildren, and pictures and letters from them would fill Chava's heart with a terrible ache and her eyes with tears.

And now suddenly she was free to go, but she felt old and afraid of a new life. Many of her pupils were leaving, but she found she could not jump at this sudden opportunity, this golden gift after all the years of anguish and loneliness. She would go on a holiday she decided, to see the family and perhaps, if she had the strength, a little of the country.

In a state of uncertainty and confusion, she went to visit Asher's grave. It turned out to be one of her last visits to Odessa's Jewish cemetery. For the first time in many years, she felt Asher's presence strongly, as if he were sitting next to her and she could talk to him.

"What shall I do, Asherel?" she asked him. "I'm sixty-three years old, too old to move and start a new life. Who knows whether I can be happy in that hot country in the Middle East, even if all the children and grandchildren are there. I've dreamed about going all these years, but now I'm not so sure. And who will tend your grave if I should leave?"

Perhaps she imagined his reply or perhaps he really was there with her. Whatever the case, it seemed he answered 'Chava, my darling, wherever you are, I'm with you. Go and meet our grandchildren and you'll be surprised at how much strength and enthusiasm they'll give you!'

As she made her way back to her little apartment on Rozumovsky Boulevard, Chava found herself looking at Odessa through the eyes of one who knows she will soon depart.

Today, she decided, she would stop in town and gaze at the sea. She did not have the strength to go down the Potjomkin Staircase - it would mean having to climb the hundred and ninety-two steps again - so she walked along Mother-in-Law Bridge.

Ah, look how beautiful the Black Sea was. None of them had enjoyed the beach enough. She hoped she would be able to live somewhere near the Mediterranean in Israel. The sea gave her a sense of timelessness, of calm.

Her eyes turned towards the harbour. Yes, that was where she and her parents had said goodbye to her brother Maish. It was where she and Marina had hopped onto ferry boats to take the children to Laungeron Beach. When the children were older, they would go on their own. It was where Yossel and Bashi had found their way to freedom.

Oh, she thought, I must go to the Opera Theatre one last time. We have all been uplifted there, especially when Yiddish theatre, dance and folk singing groups were allowed. Her mind wandered back further. It was the beautiful music Yossel had heard there which moved him to speak for the first time.

She would visit the new theatre, too, so she could tell the children about it. It was a modern building, nothing as lavish and beautiful as the old one, but, of course, the children would like to hear about it.

Summer had passed, with the acacias drooping in the heat. The winter cold was upon her but she would stay until March so she could once more enjoy the tipsy air of spring in Odessa - and then celebrate the Festival of Freedom with her family in Israel.

EPILOGUE

March, 1990. A group of volunteers stand together at the Ben Gurion Airport, waiting as hundreds of Russian immigrants arrive. Every volunteer holds a rose with which to welcome a newcomer.

Eventually, the Russians, some of whom are surrounded by family and friends, fill the airport lounge, looking exhausted and nervous. Chava is approached by a volunteer, a lady who looks about the same age as herself.

"Shalom," the lady says. "Do you understand Yiddish? I can also speak Lithuanian if that might be easier for you?"

"I understand both," replies Chava, "but I'd prefer Yiddish. I come from Odessa now, but I do remember some Lithuanian. I was born in Kovno."

"Really, me too," the volunteer says excitedly. "You look a little familiar to me. My name is Rivka Gluckman, but my maiden name was Rosen."

Chava gasps and shakes her head in disbelief. "Rivki?" she whispers. "Rivki Rosen from Kovno? And I'm Chava Aharonowitz, born Bernstein, to whom you bade farewell so many years ago at the Kovno station."

The old ladies are too overwhelmed to speak, but they embrace each other warmly. Rivka eventually remembers the rose she has and gives it to Chava.

"What happened to you during the War, Rivki? How did you manage to survive?" Chava asks.

"That is a long story, Chava. You'll have to come over to our house and I'll tell you my story, and you'll tell me yours. But now I see you have your children with you and beautiful grandchildren. Come, introduce me. Today we'll let sad memories wait until later."

GLOSSARY

All words are Hebrew unless otherwise indicated.

Aleph Beis: Hebrew alphabet

Barmitzvah: the age of thirteen at which a Jewish male becomes obligated to observe the commandments of the Torah; the celebration of this occasion

Basmitzvah: the age of twelve at which a Jewish female becomes obligated to observe the commandments of the Torah; the celebration of this occasion

Baruch Hashem: "thank G-d"

Bimah: podium in center of Synagogue

Bris Milah (Bris Milot pl.): the rite of circumcision

challa (challot pl.): special loaves of bread eaten on *Shabbos* and Festivals

chametz: leavened bread forbidden during *Pesach*

chassidim: adherents of the Chassidic movement; followers of a Rebbe

chazan: cantor

cheder (chadarim pl.): religious elementary school for boys

chupa: wedding canopy; the wedding ceremony itself

daven: to pray (Yiddish)

frum: religious (Yiddish)

gabbai (gabbaim pl.): synagogue official

Gemarah: commentary on the *Mishnah*; a volume of the Talmud

gute yohr: good year (Yiddish)

hakafah (hakafot pl.): the ritual of circling the Synagogue while carrying the Torah scrolls, on the holiday of *Simchas Torah*

hamentassen: triangular pastry eaten on Purim (Yiddish)

Hashem: G-d

Judenrein: free of Jews (a German word used during the Holocaust)

Kaddish: mourner's prayer

kashrut: Jewish dietary laws

Kiddush: benediction recited on wine on *Shabbos* and Festivals

kippa: skullcap

kosher: food fit for consumption under Jewish dietary laws

litvak: Lithuanian Jew (Yiddish)

matzah (matzos pl.): unleavened bread eaten on *Pesach* in place of yeast bread

mazal: fortune

mazeltov: lit., good fortune; congratulations

mikva: a body of water for ritual purification

minyan (minyanim pl.): quorom of ten male Jews, required for communal prayer

Mishnah (Mishnayos pl.): the primary compilation of the Oral Law first written down in the late second century C.E.; sections of the *Mishnah*

misnaged (misnagdim pl.): Jews opposed the Chassidic movement

mohel (mohelim pl.): a Jewish ritual circumcisor

Mussaf: "additional" prayer recited on a festival

Pesach: Passover, the Festival of the Exodus

Purim: the Jewish Festival of Lots

Ribbono Shel Olam: Master of the Universe

Rosh Hashanah: the Jewish New Year

Seder (Sedarim pl.): the first two nights of *Pesach* (one in Israel) when one recites the tale of the Exodus and has a feast

Shabbos (Shabbosim pl.): the Jewish Sabbath that lasts from sundown on Friday to after dark on Saturday

shammes: caretaker

Shana Tova: Good Year

Shavuos: festival occuring fifty days after *Pesach*, commemorating the the giving of the Torah

shecht: the act of slaughtering

shidduch: a match, for the purpose of marriage

Shemini Atzeret: the one day festival immediately after *Sukkot*

shemurah (matzos): *matzah* made from wheat that was guarded from the time of harvesting

shochet: ritual slaughterer

shul: synagogue (Yiddish)

siddur (siddurim pl.): prayerbook

Simchas Torah: the festival of rejoicing over the Torah, which concludes the festival of *Succot*

succah: temporary booth erected for seven days, in fulfillment of one of the commandments of *Succot*

Succot/Sukkos: the seven day Festival of Tabernacles

tallis (talleisim pl.): prayer shawl

Tatteh: Father (Yiddish)

tefillin: phylacteries

Tehillim: the book of Psalms

Tisha B'Av: the ninth day of the month of Av, a day of fasting and mourning over the destruction of the Holy Temples

Torah (Torot pl.): the five books of Moses, the written law given to the Jewish people on Mount Sinai in 1312 B.C.E.; a scroll with the words of the *Torah* written in it

Tu Bishevat: the fifteenth of the month of *Shevat*, marking a new year for trees

yarmulke: skullcap

yeshivah (yeshivot pl.): a Torah academy

Yom Kippur: day of repentance, a fast day

Yomtov: a Jewish holiday in which work is forbidden

MAP

of the areas and cities
mentioned in book

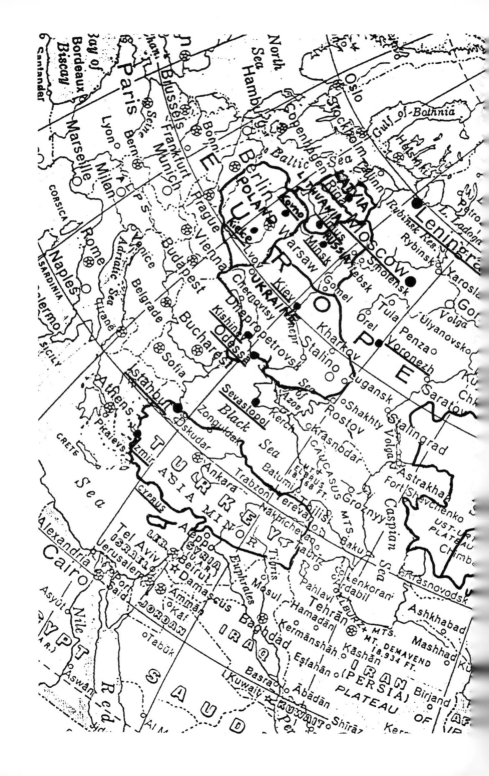